SAFETY SYMBOLS

SAFETY SYMBOLS	HAZARD	EXAMPLES	PRECAUTION	REMEDY
DISPOSAL	Special disposal procedures need to be followed.	certain chemicals, living organisms	Do not dispose of these materials in the sink or trash can.	Dispose of wastes as directed by your teacher.
BIOLOGICAL	Organisms or other biological materials that might be harmful to humans	bacteria, fungi, blood, unpreserved tissues, plant materials	Avoid skin contact with these materials. Wear mask or gloves.	Notify your teacher if you suspect contact with material. Wash hands thoroughly.
EXTREME TEMPERATURE	Objects that can burn skin by being too cold or too hot	boiling liquids, hot plates, dry ice, liquid nitrogen	Use proper protection when handling.	Go to your teacher for first aid.
SHARP OBJECT	Use of tools or glassware that can easily puncture or slice skin	razor blades, pins, scalpels, pointed tools, dissecting probes, broken glass	Practice common-sense behavior and follow guidelines for use of the tool.	Go to your teacher for first aid.
FUME	Possible danger to respiratory tract from fumes	ammonia, acetone, nail polish remover, heated sulfur, moth balls	Make sure there is good ventilation. Never smell fumes directly. Wear a mask.	Leave foul area and notify your teacher immediately.
ELECTRICAL	Possible danger from electrical shock or burn	improper grounding, liquid spills, short circuits, exposed wires	Double-check setup with teacher. Check condition of wires and apparatus.	Do not attempt to fix electrical problems. Notify your teacher immediately.
IRRITANT	Substances that can irritate the skin or mucous membranes of the respiratory tract	pollen, moth balls, steel wool, fiberglass, potassium permanganate	Wear dust mask and gloves. Practice extra care when handling these materials.	Go to your teacher for first aid.
CHEMICAL	Chemicals that can react with and destroy tissue and other materials	bleaches such as hydrogen peroxide; acids such as sulfuric acid, hydrochloric acid; bases such as ammonia, sodium hydroxide	Wear goggles, gloves, and an apron.	Immediately flush the affected area with water and notify your teacher.
TOXIC	Substance may be poisonous if touched, inhaled, or swallowed	mercury, many metal compounds, iodine, poinsettia plant parts	Follow your teacher's instructions.	Always wash hands thoroughly after use. Go to your teacher for first aid.
OPEN FLAME	Open flame may ignite flammable chemicals, loose clothing, or hair	alcohol, kerosene, potassium permanganate, hair, clothing	Tie back hair. Avoid wearing loose clothing. Avoid open flames when using flammable chemicals. Be aware of locations of fire safety equipment.	Notify your teacher immediately. Use fire safety equipment if applicable.

Eye Safety
Proper eye protection should be worn at all times by anyone performing or observing science activities.

Clothing Protection
This symbol appears when substances could stain or burn clothing.

Animal Safety
This symbol appears when safety of animals and students must be ensured.

Radioactivity
This symbol appears when radioactive materials are used.

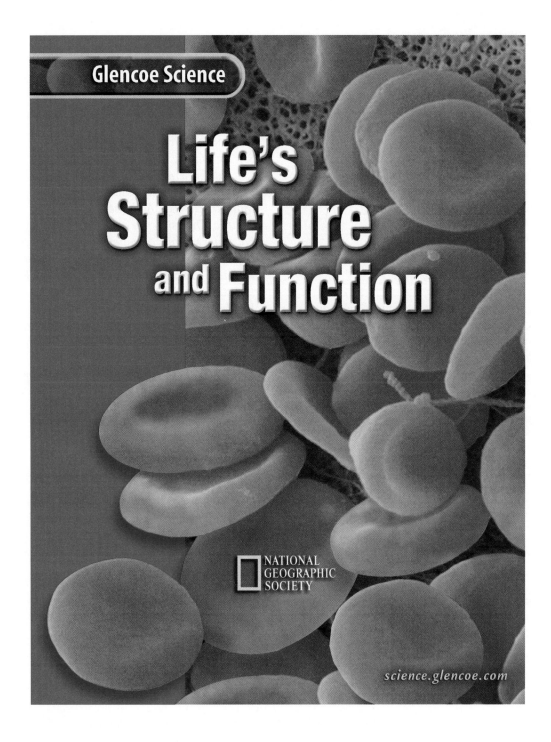

Glencoe Science

Life's Structure and Function

NATIONAL GEOGRAPHIC SOCIETY

science.glencoe.com

Glencoe McGraw-Hill

New York, New York   Columbus, Ohio   Woodland Hills, California   Peoria, Illinois

Glencoe Science

Life's Structure and Function

Student Edition
Teacher Wraparound Edition
Interactive Teacher Edition CD-ROM
Interactive Lesson Planner CD-ROM
Lesson Plans
Content Outline for Teaching
Dinah Zike's Teaching Science with Foldables
Directed Reading for Content Mastery
Foldables: Reading and Study Skills
Assessment
    Chapter Review
    Chapter Tests
    ExamView Pro Test Bank Software
    Assessment Transparencies
    Performance Assessment in the Science Classroom
    The Princeton Review Standardized Test Practice Booklet
Directed Reading for Content Mastery in Spanish
Spanish Resources
English/Spanish Guided Reading Audio Program
Reinforcement

Enrichment
Activity Worksheets
Section Focus Transparencies
Teaching Transparencies
Laboratory Activities
Science Inquiry Labs
Critical Thinking/Problem Solving
Reading and Writing Skill Activities
Mathematics Skill Activities
Cultural Diversity
Laboratory Management and Safety in the Science Classroom
Mindjogger Videoquizzes and Teacher Guide
Interactive Explorations and Quizzes CD-ROM with
    Presentation Builder
Vocabulary Puzzlemaker Software
Cooperative Learning in the Science Classroom
Environmental Issues in the Science Classroom
Home and Community Involvement
Using the Internet in the Science Classroom

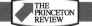

THE PRINCETON REVIEW

"Study Tip," "Test-Taking Tip," and the "Test Practice" features in this book were written by The Princeton Review, the nation's leader in test preparation. Through its association with McGraw-Hill, The Princeton Review offers the best way to help students excel on standardized assessments.

The Princeton Review is not affiliated with Princeton University or Educational Testing Service.

Glencoe/McGraw-Hill

A Division of The McGraw-Hill Companies

Cover Images: These human red blood cells are part of a liquid tissue—blood.

Send all inquires to:
Glencoe/McGraw-Hill
8787 Orion Place
Columbus, OH 43240

ISBN 0-07-825553-8
Printed in the United States of America.
  2 3 4 5 6 7 8 9 10 027/043 06 05 04 03 02 01

Authors

Alton Biggs
Biology Teacher
Allen High School
Allen, Texas

Lucy Daniel, PhD
Teacher/Consultant
Rutherfordton-Spindale High School
Rutherfordton, North Carolina

Dinah Zike
Educational Consultant
Dinah-Might Activities, Inc.
San Antonio, Texas

Content Consultants

Leanne Field, PhD
Lecturer Molecular Genetics and
Microbiology
University of Texas
Austin, Texas

Connie Rizzo, MD
Professor of Biology
Pace University
New York, New York

Homer Montgomery, PhD
Department of GeoSciences
University of Texas at Dallas
Richardson, Texas

Dominic Salinas, PhD
Middle School Science Supervisor
Caddo Parish Schools
Shreveport, Louisiana

Safety Consultant

Sandra West, PhD
Associate Professor of Biology
Southwest Texas State University
San Marcos, Texas

Math Consultant

Teri Willard, EdD
Department of Mathematics
Montana State University
Belgrade, Montana

Reading Consultants

Elizabeth Babich
Special Education Teacher
Mashpee Public Schools
Mashpee, Massachusetts

Carol A. Senf, PhD
Associate Professor of English
Georgia Institute of Technology
Atlanta, Georgia

Reviewers

Maureen Barrett
Thomas E. Harrington Middle School
Mt. Laurel, New Jersey

Diane Lutz
Denmark Middle School
Denmark, Wisconsin

Janice Bowman
Coke R. Stevenson Middle School
San Antonio, Texas

Amy Morgan
Berry Middle School
Hoover, Alabama

Cory Fish
Burkholder Middle School
Henderson, Nevada

Michelle Punch
Northwood Middle School
Houston, Texas

Linda V. Forsyth
Merrill Middle School
Denver, Colorado

Billye Robbins
Lomax Junior High School
LaPorte, Texas

Tammy Ingraham
Westover Park Intermediate School
Canyon, Texas

Delores Stout
Bellefonte Middle School
Bellefonte, Pennsylvania

Series Activity Testers

José Luis Alvarez, PhD
Math/Science Mentor Teacher
Yseleta ISD
El Paso, Texas

Mary Helen Mariscal-Cholka
Science Teacher
William D. Slider Middle School
El Paso, Texas

Nerma Coats Henderson
Teacher
Pickerington Jr. High School
Pickerington, Ohio

José Alberto Marquez
TEKS for Leaders Trainer
Yseleta ISD
El Paso, Texas

Science Kit and Boreal Laboratories
Tonawanda, New York

CONTENTS

CONTENTS

Adaptations over Time—154

Interdisciplinary Connections/Activities

Feature Contents

Activities/Science Connections

THE PRINCETON REVIEW

Feature Contents

Genome Sequencing

Figure 1
The DNA in your cells makes up your genetic material.

Your genome determines your traits—everything from your eye color and blood type to the likelihood that you might get certain diseases. A genome is the set of genes in a one-celled or many-celled organism. Each gene plays a part in the expression of a specific trait. Organisms like protists, fungi, plants, and animals have their genes on chromosomes in the nucleus of each cell. In the human genome, there are 30,000 to 40,000 genes on 23 pairs of chromosomes.

Sequencing the genome of any organism—bacteria, protist, fungus, plant, or animal—is complex. Each gene's message involves four chemicals called bases—adenine (A), cytosine (C), guanine (G), and thymine (T). The bases are linked in pairs, adenine with thymine and cytosine with guanine. Each gene is a unique chain of paired bases. The average size of a human gene is about 3,000 paired bases. The sequence carries instructions for making a specific protein. Depending on the string of bases in a gene, the protein might control the formation of a certain type of tissue or it might be an enzyme that drives a biochemical reaction. Many human disorders and diseases including Huntington's Disease and sickle cell anemia are the result of a person's genetic make up.

Figure 2
99.99% of all human genes are the same from individual to individual. It takes only 0.01% of your genes for your unique combination of traits.

Decoding the Genome

To decode a genome, scientists first have to identify the bases and their correct sequence. Then they must determine which parts of the sequence are genes. Only 3 percent of the human genome are useful genes.

Powerful supercomputers and inventive software make it possible to collect, sequence, and analyze genetic data faster than ever before. In one method, scientists mark chromosomes and then cut them into manageable fragments. Through chemical processes, each of the bases is dyed a different color then displayed in a pattern read by super-fast machines. The machines convert the base sequences into digital data. A super-computer then puts the fragments in the proper sequence, using markers from the first stage of the process.

By March 2001, the complete genome of some organisms in every kingdom—eubacteria, archaebacteria, protists, fungi, plants, and animals—was known including the human genome. These accomplishments would not have been possible without modern computer technology and the research of many scientists worldwide.

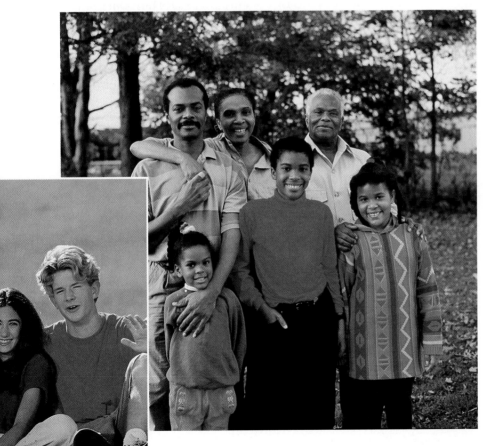

Figure 3
The genetic material passed from parents to offspring determines individual characteristics.

Science

Scientists often collect and analyze data to find answers to questions or solve problems. When you collect data and analyze it to answer questions or solve problems, you are doing science.

Genetics is a part of life science, the study of all Earth's living organisms. It includes zoology and botany. In this book, you'll learn about the structures that make up organisms, including genes, and their functions.

Science Today

Through science, scientists now have a better understanding than ever before of the world and its inhabitants. New scientific discoveries build on many that came before them. Future scientists might work to understand the long lines of genetic code that today's scientists have uncovered. Each step in decoding genomes will add to the understanding of what each of the genes does. Understanding the human genome is an important key to solving many medical problems. Some day, it might be possible to genetically identify health problems in advance and treat them before they develop.

Improved technology is another important part of science. Many advances in science would not be possible without new equipment to perform experiments and collect data. Sequencing the human genome would be impossible without the technology that allows scientists to see, manipulate, and record the genetic material. Sequencing machines and supercomputers have allowed scientists to map the human genome more quickly and accurately than was previously possible. The transfer of computerized data over the Internet also has made it possible for the Human Genome Project's scientists to share the details of their results instantly.

Figure 4
These machines, called 3700s, ran nonstop to sequence the human genome. They filter the DNA and digitally record it.

Benefits for Society

New scientific discoveries often benefit society. Science has made work easier, has helped to keep people safer, and led to medical advances that allow people to live longer and healthier lives. Scientists working on the Human Genome Project hope that their work will help provide a better explanation of how living organisms are constructed and how they function. A complete understanding of the genome will tell us more about the physical makeup of humans than we have ever known before.

Where Do Scientists Work?

Scientists work in a variety of places for a variety of reasons. Most of the American scientists who sequenced the human genome worked for either the United States government as part of the federally funded Human Genome Project, or for private companies. Both groups have the same goal even though their methods vary. These scientists worked with sensitive equipment in university laboratories and research centers. Scientists, who apply genetic research to medicine, work with the data provided by the new genetic maps. They might test hypotheses about genetic therapy through clinical experimentation.

Figure 5
Some results from the Human Genome Project are available on the Internet.

A Geneticist

Dr. John Carpten is a molecular geneticist working on the Human Genome Project. His focus is on the gene that makes some men at higher risk for developing prostate cancer. Geneticists like Dr. Carpten may do research in laboratories, analyze data in lab settings, or do diagnostic work with patients.

Dr. John Carpten

The human genome is sequenced and the locations of genes for human traits and illnesses are known. If you had the power to choose a project that uses the genome map to create something new or solve a problem, what would you choose to do and why? How would the sequenced genome help you?

Figure 6
Some day, a physician might consult a patient's genome before prescribing medicine or other treatment for a disease.

Exploring and Classifying Life

How many different living things do you see in this picture? Did your answer include the living coral? What do all living things have in common? How are they different? In this chapter, you will read the answers to these questions. You also will read how living things are classified. In the first part of the chapter, you will read how scientific methods may be used to solve many everyday and scientific problems.

What do you think?

Science Journal Look at the picture below with a classmate. Discuss what you think these might be. Here's a hint: *You could really clean up with these things.* Write your answer or best guess in your Science Journal.

Life scientists discover, describe, and name hundreds of organisms every year. How do they decide if a certain plant belongs to the iris or orchid family of flowering plants, or if an insect is more like a grasshopper or a beetle?

Use features to classify organisms

1. Observe the organisms on the opposite page or in an insect collection in your class.
2. Decide which feature could be used to separate the organisms into two groups, then sort the organisms into the two groups.
3. Continue to make new groups using different features until each organism is in a category by itself.

Observe

What features would you use to classify the living thing in the photo above? How do you think scientists classify living things? List your ideas in your Science Journal.

Before You Read

FOLDABLES
Reading & Study Skills

Making a Vocabulary Study Fold To help you study the interactions of life, make the following vocabulary Foldable. Knowing the definition of vocabulary words in a chapter is a good way to ensure you have understood the content.

1. Place a sheet of notebook paper in front of you so that the short side is at the top. Fold the paper in half from the left to the right side.
2. Through one thickness of paper, cut along every third line from the outside edge to the center fold, forming ten tabs as shown.
3. On the front of each tab, write a vocabulary word listed on the first page of each section in this chapter. On the back of each tab, write what you think the word means. Add to or change the definitions as you read.

What is science?

As You Read

What You'll Learn

- **Apply** scientific methods to problem solving.
- **Demonstrate** how to measure using scientific units.

Vocabulary

scientific methods   variable
hypothesis   theory
control   law

Why It's Important

Learning to use scientific methods will help you solve ordinary problems in your life.

The Work of Science

Movies and popcorn seem to go together. So before you and your friends watch a movie, sometimes you pop some corn in a microwave oven. When the popping stops, you take out the bag and open it carefully. You smell the mouthwatering, freshly popped corn and avoid hot steam that escapes from the bag. What makes the popcorn pop? How do microwaves work and make things hot? By the way, what are microwaves anyway?

Asking questions like these is one way scientists find out about anything in the world and the universe. Science is often described as an organized way of studying things and finding answers to questions.

Types of Science Many types of science exist. Each is given a name to describe what is being studied. For example, energy and matter have a relationship. That's a topic for physics. A physicist could answer most questions about microwaves.

On the other hand, a life scientist might study any of the millions of different animals, plants, and other living things on Earth. Look at the objects in **Figure 1.** What do they look like to you? A life scientist could tell you the objects are living plants and not just pretty rocks. Life scientists who study plants are botanists, and those who study animals are zoologists. What do you suppose a bacteriologist studies?

Figure 1

Are these all rocks? **Examine the picture carefully. Some of these objects are actually *Lithops* plants. They commonly are called stone plants and are native to deserts in South Africa.**

Critical Thinking

Whether or not you become a trained scientist, you are going to solve problems all your life. You probably solve many problems every day when you sort out ideas about what will or won't work. Suppose your CD player stops playing music. To figure out what happened, you have to think about it. That's called critical thinking, and it's the way you use skills to solve problems.

If you know that the CD player does not run on batteries and must be plugged in to work, that's the first thing you check to solve the problem. You check and the player is plugged in so you eliminate that possible solution. You separate important information from unimportant information—that's a skill. Could there be something wrong with the first outlet? You plug the player into a different outlet, and your CD starts playing. You now know that it's the first outlet that doesn't work. Identifying the problem is another skill you have.

Solving Problems

Scientists use the same types of skills that you do to solve problems and answer questions. Although scientists don't always find the answers to their questions, they always use critical thinking in their search. Besides critical thinking, solving a problem requires organization. In science, this organization often takes the form of a series of procedures called **scientific methods**. **Figure 2** shows one way that scientific methods might be used to solve a problem.

State the Problem Suppose a veterinary technician wanted to find out whether different types of cat litter cause irritation to cats' skin. What would she do first? The technician begins by observing something she cannot explain. A pet owner brings his four cats to the clinic to be boarded while he travels. He leaves his cell phone number so he can be contacted if any problems arise. When they first arrive, the four cats seem healthy. The next day however, the technician notices that two of the cats are scratching and chewing at their skin. By the third day, these same two cats have bare patches of skin with red sores. The technician decides that something in the cats' surroundings or their food might be irritating their skin.

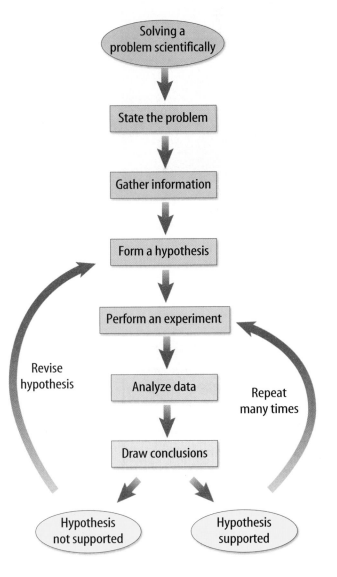

Figure 2
The series of procedures shown below is one way to use scientific methods to solve a problem.

Figure 3
Observations can be made in many different settings.

A Laboratory investigations

B Computer models

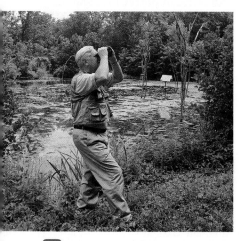

C Fieldwork

SCIENCE
Online

Research Visit the Glencoe Science Web site at **science.glencoe.com** for more information about how scientists use controlled experiments. Communicate to your class what you learn.

Gather Information Laboratory observations and experiments are ways to collect information. Some data also are gathered from fieldwork. Fieldwork includes observations or experiments that are done outside of the laboratory. For example, the best way to find out how a bird builds a nest is to go outside and watch it. **Figure 3** shows some ways data can be gathered.

The technician gathers information about the problem by watching the cats closely for the next two days. She knows that cats sometimes change their behavior when they are in a new place. She wants to see if the behavior of the cats with the skin sores seems different from that of the other two cats. Other than the scratching and chewing, all four cats' behavior seems to be the same.

The technician calls the owner and tells him about the problem. She asks him what brand of cat food he feeds his cats. Because his brand is the same one used at the clinic, she decides that food is not the cause of the skin irritation. She decides that the cats probably are reacting to something in their surroundings. There are many things in the clinic that the cats might react to. How does she decide what it is?

During her observations she notices that the cats seem to scratch and chew themselves most after using their litter boxes. The cat litter used by the clinic contains a deodorant. The technician calls the owner and finds out that the cat litter he buys does not contain a deodorant.

Form a Hypothesis Based on this information, the next thing the veterinary technician does is form a hypothesis. A **hypothesis** is a prediction that can be tested. After discussing her observations with the clinic veterinarian, she hypothesizes that something in the cat litter is irritating the cats' skin.

Test the Hypothesis with an Experiment The technician gets the owner's permission to test her hypothesis by performing an experiment. In an experiment, the hypothesis is tested using controlled conditions. The technician reads the labels on two brands of cat litter and finds that the ingredients of each are the same except that one contains a deodorant.

Controls The technician separates the cats with sores from the other two cats. She puts each of the cats with sores in a cage by itself. One cat is called the experimental cat. This cat is given a litter box containing the cat litter without deodorant. The other cat is given a litter box that contains cat litter with deodorant. The cat with deodorant cat litter is the control.

A **control** is the standard to which the outcome of a test is compared. At the end of the experiment, the control cat will be compared with the experimental cat. Whether or not the cat litter contains deodorant is the variable. A **variable** is something in an experiment that can change. An experiment should have only one variable. Other than the difference in the cat litter, the technician treats both cats the same.

✓ Reading Check *How many variables should an experiment have?*

Analyze Data The veterinary technician observes both cats for one week. During this time, she collects data on how often and when the cats scratch or chew, as shown in **Figure 4**. These data are recorded in a journal. The data show that the control cat scratches and chews more often than the experimental cat does. The sores on the skin of the experimental cat begin to heal, but those on the control cat do not.

Draw Conclusions The technician then draws the conclusion—a logical answer to a question based on data and observation—that the deodorant in the cat litter probably irritated the skin of the two cats. To accept or reject the hypothesis is the next step. In this case, the technician accepts the hypothesis. If she had rejected it, new experiments would have been necessary.

Although the technician decides to accept her hypothesis, she realizes that to be surer of her results she should continue her experiment. She should switch the experimental cat with the control cat to see what the results are a second time. If she did this, the healed cat might develop new sores. She makes an ethical decision and chooses not to continue the experiment. Ethical decisions, like this one, are important in deciding what science should be done.

Mini LAB

Analyzing Data

Procedure
1. Obtain a **pan balance.** Follow your teacher's instructions for using it.
2. Record all data in your **Science Journal.**
3. Measure and record the mass of a dry **sponge.**
4. Soak this sponge in **water.** Measure and record its mass.
5. Calculate how much water your sponge absorbed.
6. Combine the class data and calculate the average amount of water absorbed.

Analysis
What other information about the sponges might be important when analyzing the data from the entire class?

Figure 4
Collecting and analyzing data is part of scientific methods.

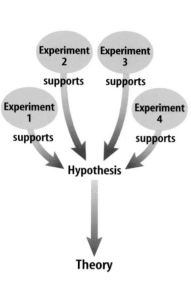

Figure 5
If data collected from several experiments over a period of time all support the hypothesis, it can finally be called a theory.

Report Results When using scientific methods, it is important to share information. The veterinary technician calls the cats' owner and tells him the results of her experiment. She tells him she has stopped using the deodorant cat litter.

The technician also writes a story for the clinic's newsletter that describes her experiment and shares her conclusions. She reports the limits of her experiment and explains that her results are not final. In science it is important to explain how an experiment can be made better if it is done again.

Developing Theories

After scientists report the results of experiments supporting their hypotheses, the results can be used to propose a scientific theory. When you watch a magician do a trick you might decide you have an idea or "theory" about how the trick works. Is your idea just a hunch or a scientific theory? A scientific **theory** is an explanation of things or events based on scientific knowledge that is the result of many observations and experiments. It is not a guess or someone's opinion. Many scientists repeat the experiment. If the results always support the hypothesis, the hypothesis can be called a theory, as shown in **Figure 5.**

☑ **Reading Check** *What is a theory based on?*

A theory usually explains many hypotheses. For example, an important theory in life sciences is the cell theory. Scientists made observations of cells and experimented for more than 100 years before enough information was collected to propose a theory. Hypotheses about cells in plants and animals are combined in the cell theory.

A valid theory raises many new questions. Data or information from new experiments might change conclusions and theories can change. Later in this chapter you will read about the theory of spontaneous generation and how this theory changed as scientists used experiments to study new hypotheses.

Laws A scientific **law** is a statement about how things work in nature that seems to be true all the time. Although laws can be modified as more information becomes known, they are less likely to change than theories. Laws tell you what will happen under certain conditions but do not necessarily explain why it happened. For example, in life science you might learn about laws of heredity. These laws explain how genes are inherited but do not explain how genes work. Due to the great variety of living things, laws that describe them are few. It is unlikely that a law about how all cells work will ever be developed.

Scientific Methods Help Answer Questions You can use scientific methods to answer all sorts of questions. Your questions may be as simple as "Where did I leave my house key?" or as complex as "Will global warming cause the polar ice caps to melt?" You probably have had to find the answer to the first question. Someday you might try to find the answer to the second question. Using these scientific methods does not guarantee that you will get an answer. Often scientific methods just lead to more questions and more experiments. That's what science is about—continuing to look for the best answers to your questions.

Problem-Solving Activity

Does temperature affect the rate of bacterial reproduction?

Some bacteria make you sick. Other bacteria, however, are used to produce foods like cheese and yogurt. Understanding how quickly bacteria reproduce can help you avoid harmful bacteria and use helpful bacteria. It's important to know things that affect how quickly bacteria reproduce. How do you think temperature will affect the rate of bacterial reproduction? A student makes the hypothesis that bacteria will reproduce more quickly as the temperature increases.

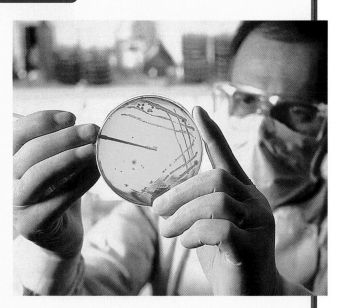

Identifying the Problem

The table below lists the reproduction-doubling rates at specific temperatures for one type of bacteria. A rate of 2.0 means that the number of bacteria doubled two times that hour (e.g., 100 to 200 to 400).

Bacterial Reproductive Rates	
Temperature (°C)	Doubling Rate per Hour
20.5	2.0
30.5	3.0
36.0	2.5
39.2	1.2

Look at the table. What conclusions can you draw from the data?

Solving the Problem

1. Do the data in the table support the student's hypothesis?
2. How would you write a hypothesis about the relationship between bacterial reproduction and temperature?
3. Make a list of other factors that might have influenced the results in the table.
4. Are you satisfied with these data? List other things that you wish you knew.
5. Describe an experiment that would help you test these other ideas.

Figure 6
Your food often is measured in metric units.

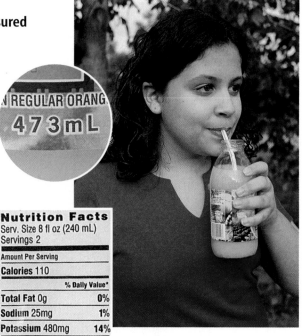

A The label of this juice bottle shows you that it contains 473 mL of juice.

N REGULAR ORANG.
473mL

B Nutritional information on the label is listed in grams or milligrams.

Nutrition Facts
Serv. Size 8 fl oz (240 mL)
Servings 2

Amount Per Serving
Calories 110

	% Daily Value*
Total Fat 0g	0%
Sodium 25mg	1%
Potassium 480mg	14%
Total Carb 27g	9%
Sugars 24g	
Protein 0g	

Vitamin C 100% • Thiamin 8%

Not a significant source of fat cal., sat. fat, cholest., fiber, vitamin A, calcium and iron.

*Percent Daily Values are based on a 2,000 calorie diet.

Measuring with Scientific Units

An important part of most scientific investigations is making accurate measurements. Think about things you use every day that are measured. Ingredients in your hamburger, hot dog, potato chips, or soft drink are measured in units such as grams and milliliters, as shown in **Figure 6.** The water you drink, the gas you use, and the electricity needed for a CD player are measured, too.

In your classroom or laboratory this year, you will use the same standard system of measurement scientists use to communicate and understand each other's research and results. This system is called the International System of Units, or SI. For example, you may need to calculate the distance a bird flies in kilometers. Perhaps you will be asked to measure the amount of air your lungs can hold in liters or the mass of an automobile in kilograms. Some of the SI units are shown in **Table 1.**

Table 1 Common SI Measurements

Measurement	Unit	Symbol	Equal to
Length	1 millimeter	mm	0.001 (1/1,000) m
	1 centimeter	cm	0.01 (1/100) m
	1 meter	m	1 m
	1 kilometer	km	1,000 m
Volume	1 milliliter	mL	0.001 (1/1,000) L
	1 liter	L	1,000 mL
Mass	1 gram	g	1,000 mg
	1 kilogram	kg	1,000 g
	1 tonne	t	1,000 kg = 1 metric ton

Safety First

Doing science is usually much more interesting than just reading about it. Some of the scientific equipment that you will use in your classroom or laboratory is the same as what scientists use. Laboratory safety is important. In many states, a student can participate in a laboratory class only when wearing proper eye protection. Don't forget to wash your hands after handling materials. Following safety rules, as shown in **Figure 7,** will protect you and others from injury during your lab experiences. Symbols used throughout your text will alert you to situations that require special attention. Some of these symbols are shown below. A description of each symbol is in the Safety Symbols chart at the front of this book.

Figure 7
Proper eye protection should be worn whenever you see this safety symbol.

Section 1 Assessment

1. Identify steps that might be followed when using scientific methods.

2. Why is it important to test only one variable at a time during an experiment?

3. What SI unit would you use to measure the width of your classroom?

4. How is a theory different than a hypothesis?

5. **Think Critically** Can the veterinary technician in this section be sure that the deodorant caused the cats' skin problems? What could she change in her experiment to make it better?

Skill Builder Activities

6. **Communicating** Write a newsletter article that explains what the veterinary technician discovered from her experiment. **For more help, refer to the** Science Skill Handbook.

7. **Converting Units** Sometimes temperature is measured in Fahrenheit degrees. Normal human body temperature is 98.6°F. What is this temperature in degrees Celsius? Use the English to metric conversion chart at the back of this book. **For more help, refer to the** Math Skill Handbook.

Living Things

Magnification: 106×

Muscle cells

What are living things like?

What does it mean to be alive? If you walked down your street after a thunderstorm, you'd probably see earthworms on the sidewalk, birds flying, clouds moving across the sky, and puddles of water. You'd see living and nonliving things that are alike in some ways. For example, birds and clouds move. Earthworms and water feel wet when touched. Yet, clouds and water are nonliving things, and birds and earthworms are living things. Any living thing is called an **organism.**

Organisms vary in size from the microscopic bacteria in mud puddles to gigantic oak trees and are found just about everywhere. They have different behaviors and food needs. In spite of these differences, all organisms have similar traits. These traits determine what it means to be alive.

Living Things Are Organized If you were to look at almost any part of an organism, like a plant leaf or your skin, under a microscope, you would see that it is made up of small units called cells. A **cell** is the smallest unit of an organism that carries on the functions of life. Some organisms are composed of just one cell while others are composed of many cells. Cells take in materials from their surroundings and use them in complex ways. Each cell has an orderly structure and contains hereditary material. The hereditary material contains instructions for cellular organization and function. **Figure 8** shows some organisms that are made of many cells. All the things that these organisms can do are possible because of what their cells can do.

Nerve cells

Figure 8
Your body is organized into many different types of cells. Two types are shown.

Magnification: 2,000×

Living Things Respond Living things interact with their surroundings. Watch your cat when you use your electric can opener. Does your cat come running to find out what's happening even when you're not opening a can of cat food? The cat in **Figure 9** ran in response to a stimulus—the sound of the can opener. Anything that causes some change in an organism is a stimulus (plural, *stimuli*). The reaction to a stimulus is a response. Often that response results in movement, such as when the cat runs toward the sound of the can opener. To carry on its daily activity and to survive, an organism must respond to stimuli.

Living things also respond to stimuli that occur inside them. For example, water or food levels in organisms' cells can increase or decrease. The organisms then make internal changes to keep the right amounts of water and food in their cells. Their temperature also must be within a certain range. An organism's ability to keep the proper conditions inside no matter what is going on outside the organism is called **homeostasis.** Homeostasis is a trait of all living things.

Figure 9
Some cats respond to a food stimulus even when they are not hungry. *Why does a cat come running when it hears a can opener?*

Reading Check *What are some internal stimuli living things respond to?*

Living Things Use Energy Staying organized and carrying on activities like homeostasis requires energy. The energy used by most organisms comes either directly or indirectly from the Sun. Plants and some other organisms use the Sun's energy and the raw materials carbon dioxide and water to make food. You and most other organisms can't use the energy of sunlight directly. Instead, you take in and use food as a source of energy. You get food by eating plants or other organisms that ate plants. Most organisms, including plants, also must take in oxygen in order to release the energy of foods.

Some bacteria live at the bottom of the oceans and in other areas where sunlight cannot reach. They can't use the Sun's energy to produce food. Instead, the bacteria use energy stored in some simple chemical compounds and the raw material carbon dioxide to make food. Unlike most other organisms, many of these bacteria do not need oxygen to release the energy that is found in their food.

Research Visit the Glencoe Science Web site at **science.glencoe.com** for more information about homeostasis. Communicate to your class what you learn.

Living Things Grow and Develop When a puppy is born, it might be small enough to hold in one hand. After the same dog is fully grown, you might not be able to hold it at all. How does this happen? The puppy grows by taking in raw materials, like milk from its mother, and making more cells. Growth of many-celled organisms, such as the puppy, is mostly due to an increase in the number of cells. In one-celled organisms, growth is due to an increase in the size of the cell.

Organisms change as they grow. Puppies can't see or walk when they are first born. In eight or nine days, their eyes open, and their legs become strong enough to hold them up. All of the changes that take place during the life of an organism are called development. **Figure 10** shows how four different organisms changed as they grew.

The length of time an organism is expected to live is its life span. Adult dogs can live for 20 years and a cat for 25 years. Some organisms have a short life span. Mayflies live only one day, but a land tortoise may live for more than 180 years. Some bristlecone pine trees have been alive for more than 4,600 years. Your life span is about 80 years.

Figure 10
Complete development of an organism can take a few days or several years. The pictures below show the development of A a dog, B a human, C a pea plant, and D a butterfly.

Figure 11

Living things reproduce themselves in many different ways. **A** A *Paramecium* reproduces by dividing into two. **B** Beetles, like most insects, reproduce by laying eggs. **C** Every spore released by these puffballs can grow into a new fungus.

A

Magnification: 400×

Living Things Reproduce Cats, dogs, alligators, fish, birds, bees, and trees eventually reproduce. They make more of their own kind. Some bacteria reproduce every 20 minutes while it might take a pine tree two years to produce seeds. **Figure 11** shows some ways organisms reproduce.

Without reproduction, living things would not exist to replace those individuals that die. An individual cat can live its entire life without reproducing. However, if cats never reproduced, all cats soon would disappear.

✔ **Reading Check** *Why is reproduction important?*

What do living things need?

What do you need to live? Do you have any needs that are different from those of other living things? To survive, all living things need a place to live and raw materials. The raw materials that they require and the exact place where they live can vary.

A Place to Live An organism's surroundings limit where it can live. Not many kinds of organisms can live in extremely hot or extremely cold environments. Most cannot live at the bottom of the ocean or on the tops of mountains. All organisms also need living space in their surroundings. For example, thousands of penguins build their nests on an island. When the island becomes too crowded, the penguins fight for space and some may not find space to build nests. An organism's surroundings must provide for all of its needs.

Health

INTEGRATION

Human infants can't take care of themselves at birth. Research to find out what human infants can do at different stages of development. Make a chart that shows changes from birth to one year old.

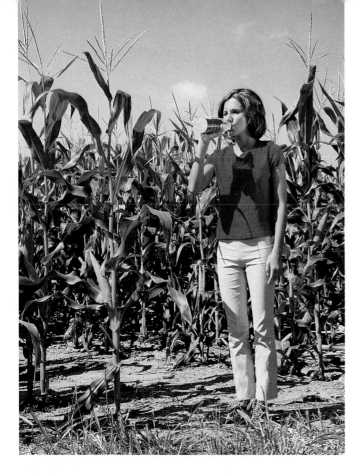

Figure 12
You and a corn plant each take in and give off about 2 L of water in a day. Most of the water you take in is from water you drink or from foods you eat. *Where do plants get water to transport materials?*

Raw Materials Water is important for all living things. Plants and animals take in and give off large amounts of water each day, as shown in **Figure 12.** Organisms use homeostasis to balance the amounts of water lost with the amounts taken in. Most organisms are composed of more than 50 percent water. You are made of 60 to 70 percent water. Organisms use water for many things. For example, blood, which is about 90 percent water, transports digested food and wastes in animals. Plants have a watery sap that transports materials between roots and leaves.

Living things are made up of substances such as proteins, fats, and sugars. Animals take in most of these substances from the foods they eat. Plants and some bacteria make them using raw materials from their surroundings. These important substances are used over and over again. When organisms die, substances in their bodies are broken down and released into the soil or air. The substances can then be used again by other living organisms. Some of the substances in your body might once have been part of a butterfly or an apple tree.

At the beginning of this section, you learned that things such as clouds, sidewalks, and puddles of water are not living things. Now do you understand why? Clouds, sidewalks, and water do not reproduce, use energy, or have other traits of living things.

Section 2 Assessment

1. What is the main source of energy used by most organisms?
2. List five traits most organisms have.
3. Why would you expect to see cells if you looked at a section of a mushroom cap under a microscope?
4. In order to survive, what things do most organisms need?
5. **Think Critically** Why is homeostasis important to organisms?

Skill Builder Activities

6. **Comparing and Contrasting** What are the similarities and differences between a goldfish and the flame of a burning candle? **For more help, refer to the** Science Skill Handbook.
7. **Using a Database** Use references to find the life span of ten animals. Use your computer to make a database. Then graph the life spans from shortest to longest. **For more help, refer to the** Technology Skill Handbook.

Where does life come from?

Life Comes from Life

You've probably seen a fish tank, like the one in **Figure 13,** that is full of algae. How did the algae get there? Before the seventeenth century, some people thought that insects and fish came from mud, that earthworms fell from the sky when it rained, and that mice came from grain. These were logical conclusions at that time, based on repeated personal experiences. The idea that living things come from nonliving things is known as **spontaneous generation.** This idea became a theory that was accepted for several hundred years. When scientists began to use controlled experiments to test this theory, the theory changed.

✔ **Reading Check** *According to the theory of spontaneous generation, where do fish come from?*

Spontaneous Generation and Biogenesis From the late seventeenth century through the middle of the eighteenth century, experiments were done to test the theory of spontaneous generation. Although these experiments showed that spontaneous generation did not occur in most cases, they did not disprove it entirely.

It was not until the mid-1800s that the work of Louis Pasteur, a French chemist, provided enough evidence to disprove the theory of spontaneous generation. It was replaced with **biogenesis** (bi oh JEN uh suhs), which is the theory that living things come only from other living things.

As You Read

What You'll Learn
- **Describe** experiments about spontaneous generation.
- **Explain** how scientific methods led to the idea of biogenesis.
- **Examine** how chemical compounds found in living things might have formed.

Vocabulary
spontaneous generation
biogenesis

Why It's Important
You can use scientific methods to try to find out about events that happened long ago or just last week. You can even use them to predict how something will behave in the future.

Figure 13
The sides of this tank were clean and the water was clear when the aquarium was set up. Algal cells, which were not visible on plants and fish, reproduced in the tank. So many algal cells are present now that the water is cloudy.

Figure 14

For centuries scientists have theorized about the origins of life. As shown on this timeline, some examined spontaneous generation—the idea that nonliving material can produce life. More recently, scientists have proposed theories about the origins of life on Earth by testing hypotheses about conditions on early Earth.

1668 Francesco Redi put decaying meat in some jars, then covered half of them. When fly maggots appeared only on the uncovered meat (see below, left), Redi concluded that they had hatched from fly eggs and had not come from the meat.

1745 John Needham heated broth in sealed flasks. When the broth became cloudy with microorganisms, he mistakenly concluded that they developed spontaneously from the broth.

1768 Lazzaro Spallanzani broiled broth in sealed flasks for a longer time than Needham did. Only the ones he opened became cloudy with contamination.

Not contaminated   Contaminated

Not contaminated

Contaminated

1859 Louis Pasteur disproved spontaneous generation by boiling broth in S-necked flasks that were open to the air. The broth became cloudy (see above, bottom right) only when a flask was tilted and the broth was exposed to dust in the S-neck.

Gases of Earth's early atmosphere

Electric current

Oceanlike mixture forms

Cools

Materials in present-day cells

1924 Alexander Oparin hypothesized that energy from the Sun, lightning, and Earth's heat triggered chemical reactions early in Earth's history. The newly-formed molecules washed into Earth's ancient oceans and became a part of what is often called the primordial soup.

1953 Stanley Miller and Harold Urey sent electric currents through a mixture of gases like those thought to be in Earth's early atmosphere. When the gases cooled, they condensed to form an oceanlike liquid that contained materials such as amino acids, found in present-day cells.

Life's Origins

Astronomy
INTEGRATION

If living things can come only from other living things, how did life on Earth begin? Some scientists hypothesize that about 5 billion years ago, Earth's solar system was a whirling mass of gas and dust. They hypothesize that the Sun and planets were formed from this mass. It is estimated that Earth is about 4.6 billion years old. Rocks found in Australia that are more than 3.5 billion years old contain fossils of once-living organisms. Where did these living organisms come from?

Oparin's Hypothesis In 1924, a Russian scientist named Alexander I. Oparin suggested that Earth's early atmosphere had no oxygen but was made up of the gases ammonia, hydrogen, methane, and water vapor. Oparin hypothesized that these gases could have combined to form the more complex compounds found in living things.

Using gases and conditions that Oparin described, American scientists Stanley L. Miller and Harold Urey set up an experiment to test Oparin's hypothesis in 1953. Although the Miller-Urey experiment showed that chemicals found in living things could be produced, it did not prove that life began in this way.

For many centuries, scientists have tried to find the origins of life, as shown in **Figure 14.** Although questions about spontaneous generation have been answered, some scientists still are investigating ideas about life's origins.

Earth Science
INTEGRATION

Scientists hypothesize that Earth's oceans originally formed when water vapor was released into the atmosphere from many volcanic eruptions. Once it cooled, rain fell and filled Earth's lowland areas. Identify five lowland areas on Earth that are now filled with water. Record your answer in your Science Journal.

Section ③ Assessment

1. Compare and contrast spontaneous generation and biogenesis.

2. Describe three controlled experiments that helped disprove the theory of spontaneous generation.

3. List one substance that was used in the Miller-Urey experiment.

4. What were the results of the Miller-Urey experiment?

5. **Think Critically** Why was Oparin's hypothesis about the origins of life important to Miller and Urey?

Skill Builder Activities

6. **Drawing Conclusions** It was thought that in the 1768 experiment some "vital force" in the broth was destroyed. Was it? Based on this experiment, what could have been concluded about where organisms come from? **For more help, refer to the** Science Skill Handbook.

7. **Using Percentages** Earth's age is estimated at 4.6 billion years old. It is estimated that life began 3.5 billion years ago. Life has been present for what percent of Earth's age? **For more help, refer to the** Math Skill Handbook.

4 How are living things classified?

As You Read

What You'll Learn

- **Describe** how early scientists classified living things.
- **Explain** the system of binomial nomenclature.
- **Demonstrate** how to use a dichotomous key.

Vocabulary

phylogeny
kingdom
binomial nomenclature
genus

Why It's Important

Knowing how living things are classified will help you understand the relationships that exist among all living things.

Classification

If you go to a library to find a book about the life of Louis Pasteur, where do you look? Do you look for it among the mystery or sports books? You expect to find a book about Pasteur's life with other biography books. Libraries group similar types of books together. When you place similar items together, you classify them. Organisms also are classified into groups.

History of Classification When did people begin to group similar organisms together? Early classifications included grouping plants that were used in medicines. Animals were often given human traits that were used to classify them such as courageous—like lions—or wise—like owls.

More than 2,000 years ago, a Greek named Aristotle observed living things. He decided that any organism could be classified as either a plant or an animal. Then he broke these two groups into smaller groups. For example, animal categories included hair or no hair, four legs or fewer legs, and blood or no blood. **Figure 15** shows some of the organisms Aristotle would have grouped together. For hundreds of years after Aristotle, no one way of classifying was accepted by everyone.

Figure 15
According to Aristotle's classification system, all animals without hair would be grouped together.
What other animals without hair would Aristotle have put in this group?

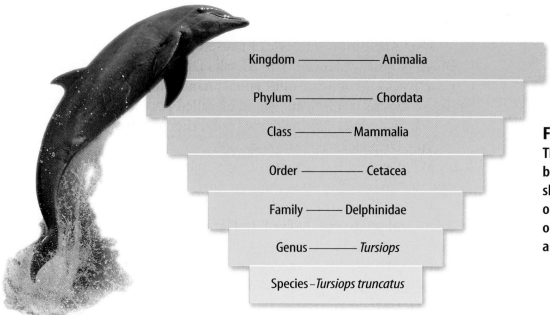

Kingdom	Animalia
Phylum	Chordata
Class	Mammalia
Order	Cetacea
Family	Delphinidae
Genus	*Tursiops*
Species	*Tursiops truncatus*

Figure 16
The classification of the bottle-nosed dolphin shows that it is in the order Cetacea. This order includes whales and porpoises.

Linnaeus In the late eighteenth century, Carolus Linnaeus, a Swedish naturalist, developed a new system of grouping organisms. His classification system was based on looking for organisms with similar structures. For example, plants that had similar flower structure were grouped together. Linnaeus's system eventually was accepted and used by most other scientists.

Modern Classification Like Linnaeus, modern scientists use similarities in structure to classify organisms. They also study fossils, hereditary information, and early stages of development. Scientists use all of this information to determine an organism's phylogeny. **Phylogeny** (fi LAH juh nee) is the evolutionary history of an organism, or how it has changed over time. Today, it is the basis for the classification of many organisms.

✔ **Reading Check** *What information would a scientist use to determine an organism's phylogeny?*

A classification system commonly used today groups organisms into six kingdoms. A **kingdom** is the first and largest category. Refer to Student Resources, Diversity of Life at the back of your text to find characteristics that place organisms into kingdoms. Kingdoms can be divided into smaller groups. The smallest classification category is a species. Organisms that belong to the same species can mate and produce fertile offspring. To understand how an organism is classified, look at the classification of the bottle-nosed dolphin in **Figure 16.** Some scientists propose that before organisms are grouped into kingdoms, they should be placed in larger groups called domains. One proposed system groups all organisms into three domains.

Data Update For an online update of domains, visit the Glencoe Science Web site at **science.glencoe.com** and select the appropriate chapter. Communicate to your class what you learn.

Scientific Names

Using common names can cause confusion. Suppose that Diego is visiting Jamaal. Jamaal asks Diego if he would like a soda. Diego is confused until Jamaal hands him a soft drink. At Diego's house, a soft drink would be called pop. Jamaal's grandmother, listening from the living room, thought that Jamaal was offering Diego an ice-cream soda.

What would happen if life scientists used only common names of organisms when they communicated with other scientists? Many misunderstandings would occur, and sometimes health and safety are involved. In **Figure 17,** you see examples of animals with common names that can be misleading. A naming system developed by Linnaeus helped solve this problem. It gave each species a unique, two-word scientific name.

Figure 17
Common names can be misleading.

Binomial Nomenclature The two-word naming system that Linnaeus used to name the various species is called **binomial nomenclature** (bi NOH mee ul • NOH mun klay chur). It is the system used by modern scientists to name organisms. The first word of the two-word name identifies the genus of the organism. A **genus** is a group of similar species. The second word of the name might tell you something about the organism—what it looks like, where it is found, or who discovered it.

In this system, the tree species commonly known as red maple has been given the name *Acer rubrum.* The maple genus is *Acer.* The word *rubrum* is Latin for red, which is the color of a red maple's leaves in the fall. The scientific name of another maple is *Acer saccharum.* The Latin word for sugar is *saccharum.* In the spring, the sap of this tree is sweet.

A Sea lions are more closely related to seals than to lions.

B Jellyfish are neither fish nor jelly. *Do you know a misleading common name?*

Figure 18
These two lizards have the same common name, iguana, but are two different species.

A

B

Uses of Scientific Names Scientific names are used for four reasons. First, they help avoid mistakes. Both of the lizards shown in **Figure 18** have the name iguana. Using binomial nomenclature, the green iguana is named *Iguana iguana*. Someone who studied this iguana, shown in **Figure 18A,** would not be confused by information he or she read about *Dispsosaurus dorsalis*, the desert iguana, shown in **Figure 18B.** Second, organisms with similar evolutionary histories are classified together. Because of this, you know that organisms in the same genus are related. Third, scientific names give descriptive information about the species, like the maples mentioned earlier. Fourth, scientific names allow information about organisms to be organized easily and efficiently. Such information may be found in a book or a pamphlet that lists related organisms and gives their scientific names.

☑ **Reading Check** *What are four functions of scientific names?*

Tools for Identifying Organisms

Tools used to identify organisms include field guides and dichotomous (di KAH toh mus) keys. Using these tools is one way you and scientists solve problems scientifically.

Many different field guides are available. You will find some field guides at the back of this book. Most have descriptions and illustrations of organisms and information about where each organism lives. You can identify species from around the world using the appropriate field guide.

TRY AT HOME
Mini LAB

Communicating Ideas

Procedure
1. Find a **magazine picture of a piece of furniture** that can be used as a place to sit and to lie down.
2. Show the picture to ten people and ask them to tell you what word they use for this piece of furniture.
3. Keep a record of the answers in your **Science Journal.**

Analysis
1. In your Science Journal, infer how using common names can be confusing.
2. How do scientific names make communication among scientists easier?

Dichotomous Keys A dichotomous key is a detailed list of identifying characteristics that includes scientific names. Dichotomous keys are arranged in steps with two descriptive statements at each step. If you learn how to use a dichotomous key, you can identify and name a species.

Did you know many types of mice exist? You can use **Table 2** to find out what type of mouse is pictured to the left. Start by choosing between the first pair of descriptions. The mouse has hair on its tail, so you go to 2. The ears of the mouse are small, so you go on to 3. The tail of the mouse is less that 25 mm. What is the name of this mouse according to the key?

Table 2 Key to Some Mice of North America

1. Tail hair	**a.** no hair on tail; scales show plainly; house mouse, *Mus musculus* **b.** hair on tail, go to 2
2. Ear size	**a.** ears small and nearly hidden in fur, go to 3 **b.** ears large and not hidden in fur, go to 4
3. Tail length	**a.** less than 25 mm; woodland vole, *Microtus pinetorum* **b.** more than 25 mm; prairie vole, *Microtus ochrogaster*
4. Tail coloration	**a.** sharply bicolor, white beneath and dark above; deer mouse, *Peromyscus maniculatus* **b.** darker above than below but not sharply bicolor; white-footed mouse, *Peromyscus leucopus*

Section ④ Assessment

1. What is the purpose of classification?
2. What were the contributions of Aristotle and Carolus Linnaeus to classification of living things?
3. How can you identify a species using a dichotomous key?
4. Why can common names cause confusion?
5. **Think Critically** Would you expect a field guide to have common names as well as scientific names? Why or why not?

Skill Builder Activities

6. **Classifying** Create a dichotomous key that identifies types of cars. **For more help, refer to the Science Skill Handbook.**
7. **Communicating** Select a field guide for trees, insects, or mammals. Select two organisms in the field guide that closely resemble each other. Use labeled diagrams to show how they are different. **For more help, refer to the Science Skill Handbook.**

Activity

Classifying Seeds

Scientists use classification systems to show how organisms are related. How do they determine which features to use to classify organisms? In this activity, you will observe seeds and use their features to classify them.

What You'll Investigate
How can the features of seeds be used to develop a key to identify the seed?

Materials
packets of seeds (10 different kinds)
hand lens
metric ruler

Goals
- **Observe** the seeds and notice their features.
- **Classify** seeds using these features.

Safety Precautions

Do not eat any seeds or put them in your mouth. Some may have been treated with chemicals.

Procedure

1. Copy the following data table in your Science Journal and record the features of each seed. Your table will have a column for each different type of seed you observe.

Seed Data		
Feature	**Type of Seed**	
Color			
Length (mm)			
Shape			
Texture			

2. Use the features to develop a key.

3. Exchange keys with another group. Can you use their key to identify seeds?

Conclude and Apply

1. How can different seeds be classified?

2. Which feature could you use to divide the seeds into two groups?

3. **Explain** how you would classify a seed you had not seen before using your data table.

4. Why is it an advantage for scientists to use a standardized system to classify organisms? What observations did you make to support your answer?

Communicating Your Data

Compare your conclusions with those of other students in your class. **For more help, refer to the** Science Skill Handbook.

Activity — *Design Your Own Experiment*

Using Scientific Methods

Brine shrimp

Brine shrimp are relatives of lobsters, crabs, crayfish, and the shrimp eaten by humans. They are often raised as a live food source in aquariums. In nature, they live in the oceans where fish feed on them. They can hatch from eggs that have been stored in a dry condition for many years. In this investigation, you will use scientific methods to find what factors affect their hatching and growth.

Recognize the Problem

How can you use scientific methods to determine whether salt affects the hatching and growth of brine shrimp?

Form a Hypothesis

Based on your observations, state a hypothesis about how salt affects the hatching and growth of brine shrimp.

Goals
- **Design** and carry out an experiment using scientific methods to infer why brine shrimp live in the ocean.
- **Observe** the jars for one week and notice whether the brine shrimp eggs hatch.

Possible Materials
500-mL, widemouthed containers (3)
brine shrimp eggs
small, plastic spoon
distilled water (500 mL)
weak salt solution (500 mL)
strong salt solution (500 mL)
labels (3)
hand lens

Safety Precautions

Protect eyes and clothing. Be careful when working with live organisms.

Test Your Hypothesis

Plan

1. As a group, agree upon the hypothesis and decide how you will test it. Identify what results will confirm the hypothesis.

2. **List** the steps that you need to test your hypothesis. Be specific. Describe exactly what you will do in each step.

3. **List** your materials.

4. **Prepare** a data table in your Science Journal to record your data.

5. Read over your entire experiment to make sure that all planned steps are in logical order.

6. **Identify** any constants, variables, and controls of the experiment.

Do

1. Make sure your teacher approves your plan before you start.

2. Carry out the experiment as planned by your group.

3. While doing the experiment, record any observations and complete the data table in your Science Journal.

4. Use a bar graph to plot your results.

Analyze Your Data

1. **Describe** the contents of each jar after one week. Do they differ from one another? How?

2. What was your control in this experiment?

3. What were your variables?

Draw Conclusions

1. Did the results support your hypothesis? Explain.

2. **Predict** the effect that increasing the amount of salt in the water would have on the brine shrimp eggs.

3. **Compare** your results with those of other groups.

*C*ommunicating
Your Data

Prepare a set of instructions on how to hatch brine shrimp to use to feed fish. Include diagrams and a step-by-step procedure.

Mon

Acari marmoset

A marmoset stands in a tree. It is about the size of a squirrel.

Deep in the heart of the rain forest lives a small, furry animal. It swings from the trees, searches for food, and sleeps nestled high in the treetop canopy. What makes this animal unique is that it never had been seen by a human being. In fact, there is a whole world of creatures as yet undiscovered by humans. Many of them reside in the Amazon rain forest.

In 2000, a scientist from Brazil's Amazon National Research Institute came across two squirrel-sized monkeys in a remote and isolated corner of the rain forest, about 2,575 km from Rio de Janeiro.

It turns out that the monkeys had never been seen before, or even known to exist.

The new species were spotted by a scientist who named them after two nearby rivers where the animals were discovered, the Manicore and the Acari. Both animals are marmosets, which is a type of monkey found only in Central and South America. Marmosets have claws instead of nails, live in trees, and use their extraordinarily long tail like an extra arm or leg. Small and light, both marmosets measure about 23 cm in length with a 38 cm tail, and weigh no more than 0.4 kg.

The Manicore marmoset has a silvery-white upper body, a light-gray cap on its head, a yellow-orange underbody, and a black tail.

Manicore marmoset

key
BUSINESS

The Amazon rain forest is home to animals waiting to be discovered

The Acari marmoset's upper body is snowy white, its gray back sports a stripe running to the knee, and its black tail flashes a bright-orange tip.

Amazin' Amazon

The Amazon Basin is a treasure trove of unique species. The Amazon River is Earth's largest body of freshwater, with 1,100 smaller tributaries. And, more than half of the world's plant and animal species live in the rain forest ecosystems.

Many of these species are found nowhere else on Earth. Scientists believe that some animals, like the newly discovered marmosets, evolved differently from other marmosets because the rivers create natural barriers that separated the animals.

The discovery reminds people of how much we have to learn about Earth's diversity of life. Even among our closest relatives, the primates, there are still new species to be discovered.

CONNECTIONS **Research and Report** Working in small groups, find out more about the Amazon rain forest. Which plants and animals live there? What products come from the rain forest? How does what happens in the Amazon rain forest affect you? Prepare a multimedia presentation.

SCIENCE
Online

For more information, visit
science.glencoe.com

Chapter **1** Study Guide

Section 1 What is science?

1. Scientists investigate observations about living and nonliving things with the help of problem-solving techniques. *What problem-solving methods would this scientist use to find out how dolphins learn?*

2. Scientists use SI measurements to gather measurable data.

3. Safe laboratory practices help you learn more about science.

Section 2 Living Things

1. Organisms are made of cells, use energy, reproduce, respond, grow, and develop.

2. Organisms need energy, water, food, and a place to live. *What raw material is limited for organisms living in a desert?*

Section 3 Where does life come from?

1. Controlled experiments over many years finally disproved the theory of spontaneous generation.

2. Pasteur's experiment proved biogenesis, which is the theory that life comes from life. *Where did the mosquito larvae in this pond come from?*

3. Oparin's hypothesis is one explanation of how life began on Earth.

Section 4 How are living things classified?

1. Classification is the grouping of ideas, information, or objects based on their similar characteristics.

2. Scientists today use phylogeny to group organisms into six kingdoms.

3. All organisms are given a two word scientific name using binomial nomenclature.

4. Dichotomous keys are used to identify specific organisms. *How would binomial nomenclature keep scientists from confusing these two beetles?*

FOLDABLES
Reading & Study Skills

After You Read

Trade vocabulary study Foldables with a classmate and quiz each other to see how many words you can define without looking under the tabs.

Visualizing Main Ideas

Use the following terms to complete an events chain concept map showing the order in which you might use a scientific method: analyze data, perform an experiment, *and* form a hypothesis.

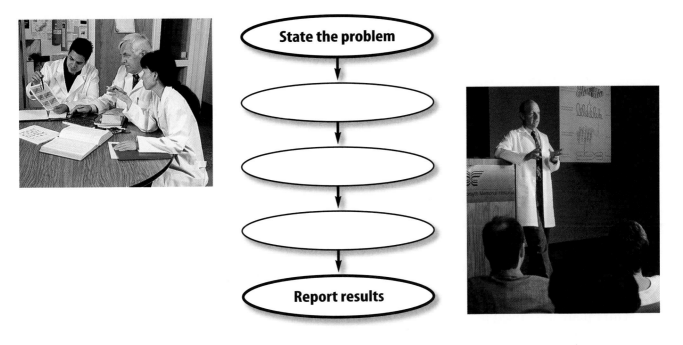

State the problem

Report results

Vocabulary Review

Vocabulary Words

a. binomial nomenclature
b. biogenesis
c. cell
d. control
e. genus
f. homeostasis
g. hypothesis
h. kingdom
i. law
j. organism
k. phylogeny
l. scientific methods
m. spontaneous generation
n. theory
o. variable

Using Vocabulary

Explain the differences in the vocabulary words in each pair below. Then explain how they are related.

1. control, variable
2. law, theory
3. biogenesis, spontaneous generation
4. binomial nomenclature, phylogeny
5. organism, cell
6. kingdom, phylogeny
7. hypothesis, scientific methods
8. organism, homeostasis
9. kingdom, genus
10. theory, hypothesis

Chapter 1 Assessment

Checking Concepts

Choose the word or phrase that best answers the question.

1. What category of organisms can mate and produce fertile offspring?
   A) family
   C) genus
   B) class
   D) species

2. What is the closest relative of *Canis lupus?*
   A) *Quercus alba*
   C) *Felis tigris*
   B) *Equus zebra*
   D) *Canis familiaris*

3. What is the source of energy for plants?
   A) the Sun
   C) water
   B) carbon dioxide
   D) oxygen

4. What makes up more than 50 percent of all living things?
   A) oxygen
   C) minerals
   B) carbon dioxide
   D) water

5. Who finally disproved the theory of spontaneous generation?
   A) Oparin
   C) Pasteur
   B) Aristotle
   D) Miller

6. What gas do some scientists think was missing from Earth's early atmosphere?
   A) ammonia
   C) methane
   B) hydrogen
   D) oxygen

7. What is the length of time an organism is expected to live?
   A) life span
   C) homeostasis
   B) stimulus
   D) theory

8. What is the part of an experiment that can be changed called?
   A) conclusion
   C) control
   B) variable
   D) data

9. What does the first word in a two-word name of an organism identify?
   A) kingdom
   C) phylum
   B) species
   D) genus

10. What SI unit is used to measure the volume of liquids?
    A) meter
    C) gram
    B) liter
    D) degree

Thinking Critically

11. How does SI help scientists in different parts of the world?

12. Using a bird as an example, explain how it has all the traits of living things.

13. Explain what binomial nomenclature is and why it is important.

14. Explain how the experiment of 1668 correctly used scientific methods to test the theory of spontaneous generation.

15. What does *Lathyrus odoratus,* the name for a sweet pea, tell you about one of its characteristics?

Developing Skills

16. **Using and Manipulating Variables and Controls** Design an experiment to test the effects of fertilizer on growing plants. Identify scientific methods used in your experiment.

17. **Forming Hypotheses** A lima bean plant is placed under a green light, another is placed under a red light, and a third under a blue light. Their growth is measured for four weeks to determine which light is best for plant growth. What are the variables in this experiment? State a hypothesis for this experiment.

18. **Comparing and Contrasting** What characteristics do an icicle and a plant share? How can you tell that the plant is a living thing and the icicle is not?

19. Interpreting Data Read the following hypothesis: Babies with a birth weight of 2.5 kg have the best chance of survival. Do the data in the following graph support this hypothesis? Explain.

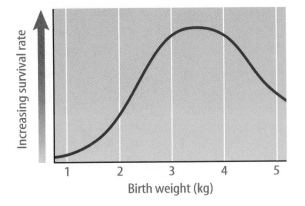

20. Classifying Which of these metric units— meter, kilometer, kilogram, or liter—is the best one to use when measuring each of the following?

A) your height

B) distance between two cities

C) how much juice is in a pitcher

D) your mass

<hr>

Performance Assessment

21. Bulletin Board Interview people in your community whose jobs require a knowledge of life science. Make a Life Science Careers bulletin board. Summarize each person's job and what he or she had to study to prepare for that job.

<hr>

TECHNOLOGY

Go to the Glencoe Science Web site at **science.glencoe.com** or use the **Glencoe Science CD-ROM** for additional chapter assessment.

<hr>

THE PRINCETON REVIEW **Test Practice**

A science class was learning about how living things respond to stimuli. Their experiment about the response of plants to light is shown below.

Day 1

Day 4

Study the experiment and answer the following questions.

1. Which hypothesis is probably being tested by this experiment?

A) Plants grow better in full light.

B) Plants prefer to grow in a box with one hole.

C) Plants can grow in any direction.

D) Plants grow toward the light.

2. After day 4, Fatima wanted to find out how plant 2 and plant 3 would grow in normal light. To do this, she would have to _____ .

A) use all new plants and boxes without holes

B) add water to all of the pots

C) remove the boxes over plant 2 and plant 3

D) put holes on all sides of the boxes

Cells

The world around you is filled with organisms that you could overlook, or even be unable to see. Some of these organisms are one-celled and some are many-celled. The monster in this photograph is a louse crawling across human skin. It can be seen in great detail with a microscope that is found in many classrooms. You can study the cells of smaller organisms with other kinds of microscopes.

What do you think?

Science Journal Look at the picture below with a classmate. Discuss what you think is happening. Here's a hint: *Not every battlefield is found on land or at sea.* Write your answer or best guess in your Science Journal.

EXPLORE ACTIVITY

If you look around your classroom, you can see many things of all sizes. With the aid of a hand lens, you can see more details. You might examine a speck of dust and discover that it is a living or dead insect. In the following activity, use a hand lens to search for the smallest thing you can find in the classroom.

Measure a small object

1. Obtain a hand lens from your teacher. Note its power (the number followed by ✕, shown somewhere on the lens frame or handle).

2. Using the hand lens, look around the room for the smallest object you can find.

3. Measure the size of the image as you see it with the hand lens. To estimate the real size of the object, divide that number by the power. For example, if it looks 2 cm long and the power is 10✕, the real length is about 0.2 cm.

Observe

In your Science Journal, describe what you observe. Did the details become clearer? Explain.

Before You Read

FOLDABLES
Reading & Study Skills

Making a Main Ideas Study Fold Make the following Foldable to help you identify the main ideas or major topics on cells.

1. Place a sheet of paper in front of you so the long side is at the top. Fold the paper in half from the left side to the right side. Then unfold.

2. Label the left side of the paper *Plant Cell*. Label the right side of the paper *Animal Cell,* as shown.

3. Before you read the chapter, draw a plant cell on the left side of the paper and an animal cell on the right side of the paper.

4. As you read the chapter, change and add to your drawings.

Cell Structure

As You Read

What You'll Learn

- **Identify** names and functions of each part of a cell.
- **Explain** how important a nucleus is in a cell.
- **Compare** tissues, organs, and organ systems.

Vocabulary

cell membrane	ribosome
cytoplasm	endoplasmic
cell wall	reticulum
organelle	Golgi body
nucleus	tissue
chloroplast	organ
mitochondrion	

Why It's Important

If you know how organelles function, it's easier to understand how cells survive.

Common Cell Traits

Living cells are dynamic and have several things in common. Cells are the smallest unit that is capable of performing life functions. All cells have an outer covering called a **cell membrane.** Inside every cell is a gelatinlike material called **cytoplasm** (SI toh plaz uhm). In the cytoplasm of every cell is hereditary material that controls the life of the cell.

Comparing Cells Cells come in many sizes. A nerve cell in your leg could be a meter long. A human egg cell is no bigger than the dot on this **i.** A human red blood cell is about one-tenth the size of a human egg cell. A bacterium is even smaller—8,000 of the smallest bacteria can fit inside one of your red blood cells.

A cell's shape might tell you something about its function. The nerve cell in **Figure 1** has many fine extensions that send and receive impulses to and from other cells. Though a nerve cell cannot change shape, muscle cells and some blood cells can. In plant stems, some cells are long and hollow and have openings at their ends. These cells carry food and water through the plant.

Figure 1
The shape of the cell can tell you something about its function. These cells are magnified 700 times their actual size.

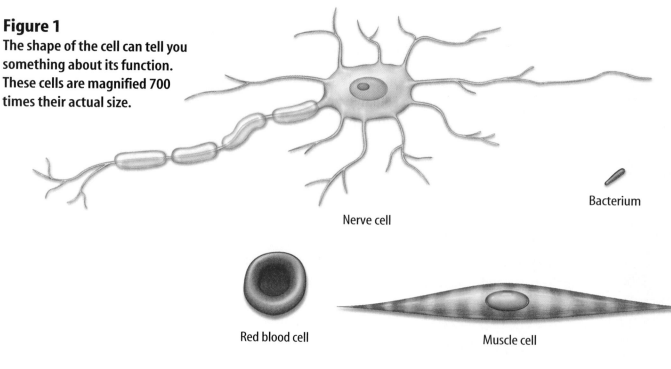

Bacterium

Nerve cell

Red blood cell

Muscle cell

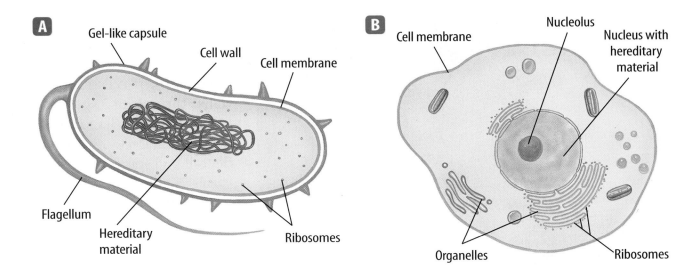

A
Gel-like capsule
Cell wall
Cell membrane
Flagellum
Hereditary material
Ribosomes

B
Cell membrane
Nucleolus
Nucleus with hereditary material
Organelles
Ribosomes

Cell Types Scientists have found that cells can be separated into two groups. One group has no membrane-bound structures inside the cell and the other group does, as shown in **Figure 2.** Cells without membrane-bound structures are called prokaryotic (proh KAYR ee yah tihk) cells. Cells with membrane-bound structures are called eukaryotic (yew KAYR ee yah tihk) cells.

✔ **Reading Check** *Into what two groups can cells be separated?*

Cell Organization

Each cell in your body has a specific function. You might compare a cell to a busy delicatessen that is open 24 hours every day. Raw materials for the sandwiches are brought in often. Some food is eaten in the store, and some customers take their food with them. Sometimes food is prepared ahead of time for quick sale. Wastes are put into trash bags for removal or recycling. Similarly, your cells are taking in nutrients, secreting and storing chemicals, and breaking down substances 24 hours every day.

Cell Wall Just like a deli that is located inside the walls of a building, some cells are enclosed in a cell wall. The cells of plants, algae, fungi, and most bacteria are enclosed in a cell wall. **Cell walls** are tough, rigid outer coverings that protect the cell and give it shape.

A plant cell wall, as shown in **Figure 3,** mostly is made up of a carbohydrate called cellulose. The long, threadlike fibers of cellulose form a thick mesh that allows water and dissolved materials to pass through it. Cell walls also can contain pectin, which is used in jam and jelly, and lignin, which is a compound that makes cell walls rigid. Plant cells responsible for support have a lot of lignin in their walls.

Figure 2
Examine these drawings of cells. **A** Prokaryotic cells are only found in one-celled organisms, such as bacteria. **B** Protists, fungi, plants and animals are made of eukaryotic cells. *What differences do you see between them?*

Figure 3
The protective cell wall of a plant cell is outside the cell membrane.

Cell wall

Figure 4
The cell membrane is made up of a double layer of fatlike molecules.

Cell membrane

Figure 5
Cytoskeleton, a network of fibers in the cytoplasm, gives cells structure and helps them maintain shape.

Modeling Cytoplasm

Procedure
1. Add 100 mL of **water** to a clear container.
2. Add **unflavored gelatin** and stir.
3. Shine a **flashlight** through the solution.

Analysis
1. Describe what you see.
2. How does a model help you understand what cytoplasm might be like?

Cell Membrane The protective layer around all cells is the cell membrane, as shown in **Figure 4.** If cells have cell walls, the cell membrane is inside of it. The cell membrane regulates interactions between the cell and the environment. Water is able to move freely into and out of the cell through the cell membrane. Food particles and some molecules enter and waste products leave through the cell membrane.

Cytoplasm Cells are filled with a gelatinlike substance called cytoplasm that constantly flows inside the cell membrane. Many important chemical reactions occur within the cytoplasm.

Throughout the cytoplasm is a framework called the cytoskeleton, which helps the cell maintain or change its shape. Cytoskeletons enable some cells to move. An amoeba, for example, moves by stretching and contracting its cytoskeleton. The cytoskeleton is made up of thin, hollow tubes of protein and thin, solid protein fibers, as shown in **Figure 5.** Proteins are organic molecules made up of amino acids.

☑ **Reading Check** *What is the function of the cytoskeleton?*

Most of a cell's life processes occur in the cytoplasm. Within the cytoplasm of eukaryotic cells are structures called **organelles.** Some organelles process energy and others manufacture substances needed by the cell or other cells. Certain organelles move materials, while others act as storage sites. Most organelles are surrounded by membranes. The nucleus is usually the largest organelle in a cell.

Nucleus The nucleus is like the deli manager who directs the store's daily operations and passes on information to employees. The **nucleus,** shown in **Figure 6,** directs all cell activities and is separated from the cytoplasm by a membrane. Materials enter and leave the nucleus through openings in the membrane. The nucleus contains the instructions for everything the cell does. These instructions are found on long, threadlike, hereditary material made of DNA. DNA is the chemical that contains the code for the cell's structure and activities. During cell division, the hereditary material coils tightly around proteins to form structures called chromosomes. A structure called a nucleolus also is found in the nucleus.

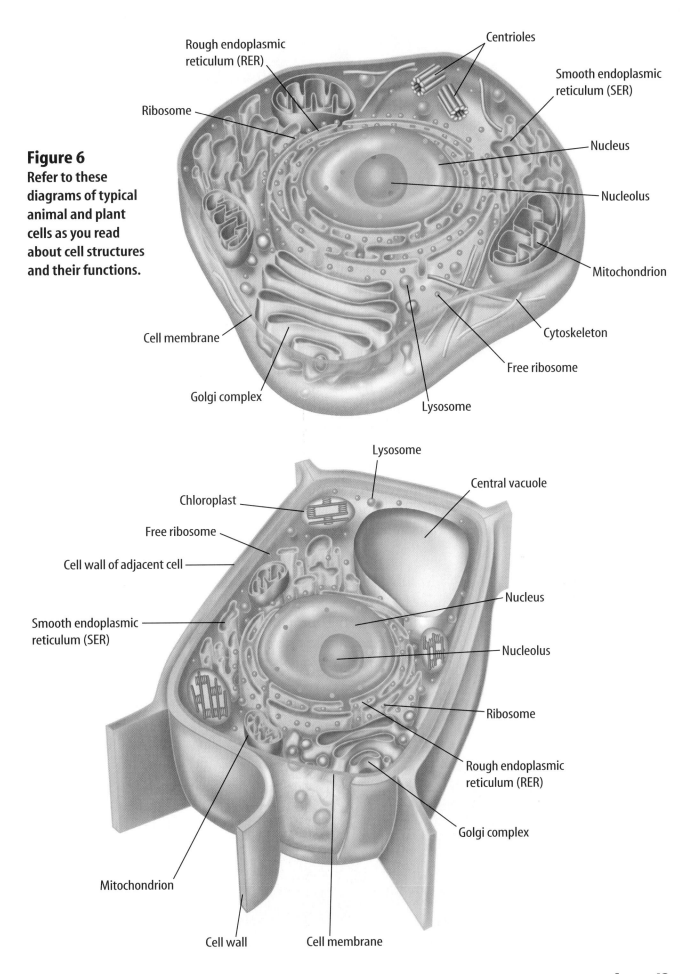

Figure 6
Refer to these diagrams of typical animal and plant cells as you read about cell structures and their functions.

Rough endoplasmic reticulum (RER)

Ribosome

Centrioles

Smooth endoplasmic reticulum (SER)

Nucleus

Nucleolus

Mitochondrion

Cytoskeleton

Free ribosome

Lysosome

Golgi complex

Cell membrane

Lysosome

Central vacuole

Chloroplast

Free ribosome

Cell wall of adjacent cell

Nucleus

Smooth endoplasmic reticulum (SER)

Nucleolus

Ribosome

Rough endoplasmic reticulum (RER)

Golgi complex

Mitochondrion

Cell wall

Cell membrane

Magnification: 37,000×

Figure 7
Chloroplasts are organelles that use sunlight to make sugar from carbon dioxide and water. They contain chlorophyll, which gives most leaves and stems their green color.

Figure 8
Mitochondria are known as the powerhouses of the cell because they release energy that is needed by the cell from food.
What types of cells might contain many mitochondria?

Physics INTEGRATION

Energy-Processing Organelles To use food to make new substances and to communicate with each other, cells require a continuous supply of energy. In plant cells, food is made in green organelles in the cytoplasm called **chloroplasts** (KLOR uh plasts), as shown in **Figure 7.** Chloroplasts contain the green pigment chlorophyll, which gives leaves and stems their green color. Chlorophyll captures light energy and uses it to make a sugar called glucose. Glucose molecules store the captured light energy as chemical energy. Many cells, including animal cells, do not have chloroplasts for making food. They must get food from their environment.

The energy in food is stored until it is released by the mitochondria. **Mitochondria** (mi tuh KAHN dree uh) (singular, *mitochondrion*), such as the one shown in **Figure 8,** are organelles where energy is released from breaking down food into carbon dioxide and water. Just as the gas or electric company supplies fuel for the deli, a mitochondrion releases energy for use by the cell. Some types of cells, such as muscle cells, are more active than other cells. These cells have large numbers of mitochondria. Why would active cells have more or larger mitochondria?

Manufacturing Organelles One substance that takes part in nearly every cell activity is protein. Proteins are part of cell membranes. Other proteins are needed for chemical reactions that take place in the cytoplasm. Cells make their own proteins on small structures called **ribosomes.** Even though ribosomes are considered organelles, they are not membrane bound. Some ribosomes float freely in the cytoplasm; and others are attached to the endoplasmic reticulum. Ribosomes are made in the nucleolus and move out into the cytoplasm. Ribosomes receive directions from the hereditary material in the nucleus on how, when, and in what order to make specific proteins.

Magnification: 48,000×

Figure 9
Endoplasmic reticulum (ER) is a complex series of membranes in the cytoplasm of the cell. *What would smooth ER look like?*

Processing, Transporting, and Storing Organelles

The **endoplasmic reticulum** (en duh PLAZ mihk • rih TIHK yuh lum) or ER, as shown in **Figure 9,** extends from the nucleus to the cell membrane. It is a series of folded membranes in which materials can be processed and moved around inside of the cell. The ER takes up a lot of space in some cells.

The endoplasmic reticulum may be "rough" or "smooth." ER that has no attached ribosomes is called smooth endoplasmic reticulum. This type of ER processes other cellular substances such as lipids that store energy. Ribsomes are attached to areas on the rough ER. There they carry out their job of making proteins that are moved out of the cell or used within the cell.

✔ **Reading Check** *What is the difference between rough ER and smooth ER?*

After proteins are made in a cell, they are transferred to another type of cell organelle called the Golgi (GAWL jee) bodies. The **Golgi bodies,** as shown ion **Figure 10,** are stacked, flattened membranes. The Golgi bodies sort proteins and other cellular substances and package them into membrane-bound structures called vesicles. The vesicles deliver cellular substances to areas inside the cell. They also carry cellular substances to the cell membrane where they are released to the outside of the cell.

Just as a deli has refrigerators for temporary storage of some its foods and ingredients, cells have membrane-bound spaces called vacuoles for the temporary storage of materials. A vacuole can store water, waste products, food, and other cellular materials. In plant cells, the vacuole may make up most of the cell's volume.

Figure 10
The Golgi body packages materials and moves them to the outside of the cell. *Why are materials removed from the cell?*

Magnification: 28,000×

Environmental Science

INTEGRATION

Just like a cell, you can recycle materials. Paper, plastics, aluminum, and glass are materials that can be recycled into usable items. Make a promotional poster to encourage others to recycle.

Recycling Organelles Active cells break down and recycle substances. Organelles called lysosomes (LI suh sohm) contain digestive chemicals that help break down food molecules, cell wastes, and worn-out cell parts. In a healthy cell, chemicals are released into vacuoles only when needed. The lysosome's membrane prevents the digestive chemicals inside from leaking into the cytoplasm and destroying the cell. When a cell dies, a lysosome's membrane disintegrates. This releases digestive chemicals that allow the quick breakdown of the cell's contents.

✓ **Reading Check** *What is the function of the lysosome's membrane?*

Math Skills Activity

Calculate the Ratio of Surface Area to Volume of Cells

Example Problem

Assume that a cell is like a cube with six equal sides. Find the ratio of surface area to volume for a cube that is 4 cm high.

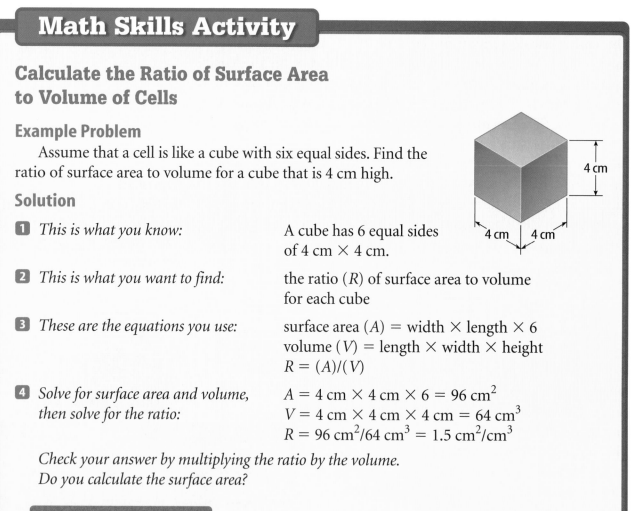

Solution

1 *This is what you know:* A cube has 6 equal sides of 4 cm × 4 cm.

2 *This is what you want to find:* the ratio (R) of surface area to volume for each cube

3 *These are the equations you use:*
surface area (A) = width × length × 6
volume (V) = length × width × height
$R = (A)/(V)$

4 *Solve for surface area and volume, then solve for the ratio:*
$A = 4 \text{ cm} \times 4 \text{ cm} \times 6 = 96 \text{ cm}^2$
$V = 4 \text{ cm} \times 4 \text{ cm} \times 4 \text{ cm} = 64 \text{ cm}^3$
$R = 96 \text{ cm}^2/64 \text{ cm}^3 = 1.5 \text{ cm}^2/\text{cm}^3$

Check your answer by multiplying the ratio by the volume. Do you calculate the surface area?

Practice Problems

1. Calculate the ratio of surface area to volume for a cube that is 2 cm high. What happens to this ratio as the size of the cube decreases?

2. If a 4-cm cube doubled just one of its dimensions—length, width, or height—what would happen to the ratio of surface area to volume?

For more help, refer to the Math Skills Handbook.

From Cell to Organism

Many one-celled organisms perform all their life functions by themselves. Cells in a many-celled organism, however, do not work alone. Each cell carries on its own life functions while depending in some way on other cells in the organism.

In **Figure 11,** you can see cardiac muscle cells grouped together to form a tissue. A **tissue** is a group of similar cells that work together to do one job. Each cell in a tissue does its part to keep the tissue alive.

Tissues are organized into organs. An **organ** is a structure made up of two or more different types of tissues that work together. Your heart is an organ made up of cardiac muscle tissue, nerve tissue, and blood tissues. The cardiac muscle tissue contracts, making the heart pump. The nerve tissue brings messages that tell the heart how fast to beat. The blood tissue is carried from the heart to other organs of the body.

✔ **Reading Check** *What type of tissues make up your heart?*

A group of organs working together to perform a certain function is an organ system. Your heart, arteries, veins, and capillaries make up your cardiovascular system. In a many-celled organism, several systems work together in order to perform life functions efficiently. Your nervous, circulatory, respiratory, muscular, and other systems work together to keep you alive.

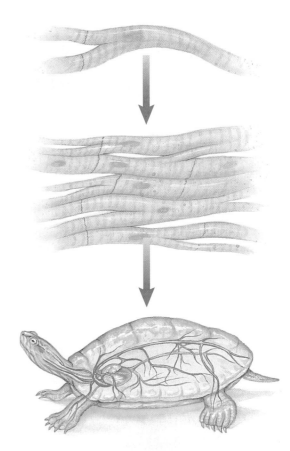

Figure 11
In many-celled organisms, cells are organized into tissues, tissues into organs, organs into systems, and systems into organisms.

Section 1 Assessment

1. Explain the important role of the nucleus in the life of a cell.

2. Compare and contrast the energy processing organelles.

3. Why are digestive enzymes in a cell enclosed in a membrane-bound organelle?

4. How are cells, tissues, organs, and organ systems related?

5. **Think Critically** How is the cell of a one-celled organism different from the cells in many-celled organisms?

Skill Builder Activities

6. **Interpreting Scientific Illustrations** Examine the illustrations of the animal cell and the plant cell in **Figure 6** and make a list of differences and similarities between them. **For more help, refer to the** Science Skill Handbook.

7. **Communicating** Your textbook compared some cell functions to that of a deli. In your Science Journal, write an essay that explains how a cell is like your school or town. **For more help, refer to the** Science Skill Handbook.

Activity

Comparing Cells

If you compared a goldfish to a rose, you would find them unlike each other. Are their individual cells different also? Try this activity to compare plant and animal cells.

What You'll Investigate
How do human cheek cells and plant cells compare?

Materials
microscope	dropper
microscope slide	*Elodea* plant
coverslip	prepared slide of human
forceps	cheek cells
tap water	

Goal
■ **Compare and contrast** an animal cell and a plant cell.

Safety Precautions

Procedure

1. Copy the data table in your Science Journal. Check off the cell parts as you observe them.

Cell Observations		
Cell Part	**Cheek**	***Elodea***
Cytoplasm		
Nucleus		
Chloroplasts		
Cell Wall		
Cell Membrane		

2. Using forceps, make a wet-mount slide of a young leaf from the tip of an *Elodea* plant.

3. **Observe** the leaf on low power. Focus on the top layer of cells.

4. Switch to high power and focus on one cell. In the center of the cell is a membrane-bound organelle called the central vacuole. Observe the chloroplasts—the green, disk-shaped objects moving around the central vacuole. Try to find the cell nucleus. It looks like a clear ball.

5. **Draw** the *Elodea* cell. Label the cell wall, cytoplasm, chloroplasts, central vacuole, and nucleus. Return to low power and remove the slide. Properly dispose of the slide.

6. **Observe** the prepared slide of cheek cells under low power.

7. Switch to high power and observe the cell nucleus. Draw and label the cell membrane, cytoplasm, and nucleus. Return to low power and remove the slide.

Conclude and Apply

1. **Compare and contrast** the shapes of the cheek cell and the *Elodea* cell.

2. What can you conclude about the differences between plant and animal cells?

Communicating Your Data

Draw the two kinds of cells on one sheet of paper. Use a green pencil to label the organelles found only in plants, a red pencil to label the organelles found only in animals, and a blue pencil to label the organelles found in both. **For more help, refer to the Science Skill Handbook.**

Viewing Cells

Magnifying Cells

The number of living things in your environment that you can't see is much greater than the number that you can see. Many of the things that you cannot see are only one cell in size. To see most cells, you need to use a microscope.

Trying to see separate cells in a leaf, like the ones in **Figure 12,** is like trying to see individual photos in a photo mosaic picture that is on the wall across the room. As you walk toward the wall, it becomes easier to see the individual photos. When you get right up to the wall, you can see details of each small photo. A microscope has one or more lenses that enlarge the image of an object as though you are walking closer to it. Seen through these lenses, the leaf appears much closer to you, and you can see the individual cells that carry on life processes.

Early Microscopes   In the late 1500s, the first microscope was made by a Dutch maker of reading glasses. He put two magnifying glasses together in a tube and got an image that was larger than the image that was made by either lens alone.

In the mid 1600s, Antonie van Leeuwenhoek, a Dutch fabric merchant, made a simple microscope with a tiny glass bead for a lens, as shown in **Figure 13.** With it, he reported seeing things in pond water that no one had ever imagined. His microscope could magnify up to 270 times. Another way to say this is that his microscope could make the image of an object 270 times larger than its actual size. Today you would say his lens had a power of 270×. Early compound microscopes were crude by today's standards. The lenses would make an image larger, but it wasn't always sharp or clear.

As You Read

What You'll Learn

- **Compare** the differences between the compound light microscope and the electron microscope.
- **Summarize** the discoveries that led to the development of the cell theory.
- **Relate** the cell theory to modern biology.

Vocabulary
cell theory

Why It's Important

Humans are like other living things because they are all made of cells.

Figure 12
Individual cells become visible when a plant leaf is viewed using a microscope with enough magnifying power.

Figure 13

Microscopes give us a glimpse into a previously invisible world. Improvements have vastly increased their range of visibility, allowing researchers to study life at the molecular level. A selection of these powerful tools—and their magnification power—is shown here.

▶ **Up to 250x**
LEEUWENHOEK MICROSCOPE **Held by a modern researcher, this historic microscope allowed Leeuwenhoek to see clear images of tiny freshwater organisms that he called "beasties."**

▼ **Up to 1,500x** BRIGHTFIELD / DARKFIELD MICROSCOPE **The light microscope is often called the brightfield microscope because the image is viewed against a bright background. A brightfield microscope is the tool most often used in laboratories to study cells. Placing a thin metal disc beneath the stage, between the light source and the objective lenses, converts a brightfield microscope to a darkfield microscope. The image seen using a darkfield microscope is bright against a dark background. This makes details more visible than with a brightfield microscope. Below are images of a *Paramecium* as seen using both processes.**

Darkfield

Brightfield

▲ **Up to 1,500x** FLUORESCENCE MICROSCOPE **This type of microscope requires that the specimen be treated with special fluorescent stains. When viewed through this microscope, certain cell structures or types of substances glow, as seen in the image of a *Paramecium* above.**

► **Up to 500,000x** TRANSMISSION ELECTRON MICROSCOPE A TEM aims a beam of electrons through a specimen. Denser portions of the specimen allow fewer electrons to pass through and appear darker in the image. Organisms, such as the *Paramecium* at right, can only be seen when the image is photographed or shown on a monitor. A TEM can magnify hundreds of thousands of times.

► **Up to 1,500x** PHASE-CONTRAST MICROSCOPE A phase-contrast microscope emphasizes slight differences in a specimen's capacity to bend light waves, thereby enhancing light and dark regions without the use of stains. This type of microscope is especially good for viewing living cells, like the *Paramecium* above left. The images from a phase-contrast microscope can only be seen when the specimen is photographed or shown on a monitor.

► **Up to 200,000x** SCANNING ELECTRON MICROSCOPE An SEM sweeps a beam of electrons over a specimen's surface, causing other electrons to be emitted from the specimen. SEMs produce realistic, three-dimensional images, which can only be viewed as photographs or on a monitor, as in the image of the *Paramecium* at right. Here a researcher compares an SEM picture to a computer monitor showing an enhanced image.

Physics
INTEGRATION

A magnifying glass is a convex lens. All microscopes use one or more convex lenses. In your Science Journal, diagram a convex lens and describe its shape.

Modern Microscopes

Scientists use a variety of microscopes to study organisms, cells, and cell parts that are too small to be seen with the human eye. Depending on how many lenses a microscope contains, it is called simple or compound. A simple microscope is similar to a magnifying glass. It has only one lens. A microscope's lens makes an enlarged image of an object and directs light toward your eye. The change in apparent size produced by a microscope is called magnification. Microscopes vary in powers of magnification. Some microscopes can make images of individual atoms.

The microscope you probably will use to study life science is a compound light microscope, similar to the one in the Reference Handbook at the back of this book. The compound light microscope has two sets of lenses—eyepiece lenses and objective lenses. The eyepiece lenses are mounted in one or two tubelike structures. Images of objects viewed through two eyepieces, or stereomicroscopes, are three-dimensional. Images of objects viewed through one eyepiece are not. Compound light microscopes usually have two to four movable objective lenses.

Magnification

The powers of the eyepiece and objective lenses determine the total magnifications of a microscope. If the eyepiece lens has a power of 10× and the objective lens has a power of 43×, then the total magnification is 430× (10× times 43×). Some compound microscopes, like those in **Figure 13,** have more powerful lenses that can magnify an object up to 2,000 times its original size.

Electron Microscopes

Things that are too small to be seen with other microscopes can be viewed with an electron microscope. Instead of using lenses to direct beams of light, an electron microscope uses a magnetic field in a vacuum to direct beams of electrons. Some electron microscopes can magnify images up to one million times. Electron microscope images must be photographed or electronically produced.

Several kinds of electron microscopes have been invented, as shown in **Figure 13.** Scanning electron microscopes (SEM) produce a realistic, three-dimensional image. Only the surface of the specimen can be observed using an SEM. Transmission electron microscopes (TEM) produce a two-dimensional image of a thinly-sliced specimen. Details of cell parts can be examined using a TEM. Scanning tunneling microscopes (STM) are able to show the arrangement of atoms on the surface of a molecule. A metal probe is placed near the surface of the specimen and electrons flow from the tip. The hills and valleys of the specimen's surface are mapped.

Development of the Cell Theory

During the seventeenth century, scientists used their new invention, the microscope, to explore the newly discovered microscopic world. They examined drops of blood, scrapings from their own teeth, and other small things. Cells weren't discovered until the microscope was improved. In 1665, Robert Hooke cut a thin slice of cork and looked at it under his microscope. To Hooke, the cork seemed to be made up of empty little boxes, which he named cells.

In the 1830s, Matthias Schleiden used a microscope to study plant parts. He concluded that all plants are made of cells. Theodor Schwann, after observing many different animal cells, concluded that all animals also are made up of cells. Eventually, they combined their ideas and became convinced that all living things are made of cells.

Several years later, Rudolf Virchow hypothesized that cells divide to form new cells. Virchow proposed that every cell came from a cell that already existed. His observations and conclusions and those of others are summarized in the **cell theory,** as described in **Table 1.**

✔ Reading Check *Who made the conclusion that all animals are made of cells?*

Table 1 The Cell Theory

All organisms are made up of one or more cells.	An organism can be one cell or many cells like most plants and animals.
The cell is the basic unit of organization in organisms.	Even in complex organisms, the cell is the basic unit of structure and function.
All cells come from cells.	Most cells can divide to form two new, identical cells.

Section 2 Assessment

1. Explain why the invention of the microscope was important in the study of cells.
2. What is stated in the cell theory?
3. What is the difference between a simple and a compound light microscope?
4. What was Virchow's contribution to the cell theory?
5. **Think Critically** Why would it be better to look at living cells than at dead cells?

Skill Builder Activities

6. **Concept Mapping** Using a network tree concept map, compare a compound light microscope to an electron microscope. **For more help, refer to the** Science Skill Handbook.
7. **Solving One-Step Equations** Calculate the magnifications of a microscope that has an $8\times$ eyepiece, and $10\times$ and $40\times$ objectives. **For more help, refer to the** Math Skill Handbook.

SECTION

③ Viruses

Figure 14
Viruses come in a variety of shapes.

What are viruses?

Cold sores, measles, chicken pox, colds, the flu, and AIDS are diseases caused by nonliving particles called viruses. A **virus** is a strand of hereditary material surrounded by a protein coating. Viruses don't have a nucleus or other organelles. They also lack a cell membrane. Viruses, as shown in **Figure 14,** have a variety of shapes. Because they are too small to be seen with a light microscope, they were discovered only after the electron microscope was invented. Before that time, scientists only hypothesized about viruses.

How do viruses multiply?

All viruses can do is make copies of themselves. However, they can't do that without the help of a living cell called a **host cell.** Crystalized forms of some viruses can be stored for years. Then, if they enter an organism, they can multiply quickly.

Once a virus is inside of a host cell, the virus can act in two ways. It can either be active or it can become latent, which is an inactive stage.

A Filoviruses do not have uniform shapes. Some of these *Ebola* viruses have a loop at one end.

B The potato leafroll virus, *Polervirus*, damages potato crops worldwide.

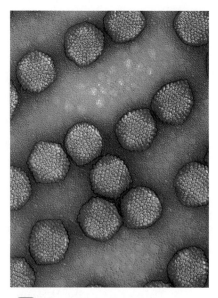

C This is just one of the many adenoviruses that can cause the common cold.

Figure 15

An active virus multiplies and destroys the host cell.
A The virus attaches to a specific host cell. **B** The virus's hereditary material enters the host cell. **C** The hereditary material of the virus causes the cell to make viral hereditary material and proteins. **D** New viruses form inside of the host cell. **E** New viruses are released as the host cell bursts open and is destroyed.

Active Viruses When a virus enters a cell and is active, it causes the host cell to make new viruses. This process destroys the host cell. Follow the steps in **Figure 15** to see one way that an active virus functions inside a cell.

Latent Viruses Some viruses can be latent. That means that after the virus enters a cell, its hereditary material can become part of the cell's hereditary material. It does not immediately make new viruses or destroy the cell. As the host cell reproduces, the viral DNA is copied. A virus can be latent for many years. Then, at any time, certain conditions, either inside or outside your body, can activate the virus.

If you have had a cold sore on your lip, a latent virus in your body has become active. The cold sore is a sign that the virus is active and destroying cells in your lip. When the cold sore disappears, the virus has become latent again. The virus is still in your body's cells, but it is hiding and doing no apparent harm.

SCIENCE *Online*

Research Visit the Glencoe Science Web site at **science.glencoe.com** for information on viruses. What environmental stimuli might activate a latent virus? Record your answer in your Science Journal.

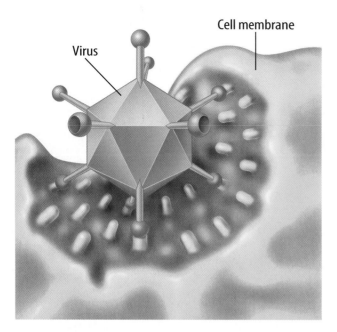

Virus

Cell membrane

Figure 16
Viruses and the attachment sites of the host cell must match exactly. That's why most viruses infect only one kind of host cell.

How do viruses affect organisms?

Viruses attack animals, plants, fungi, protists, and all prokaryotes. Some viruses can infect only specific kinds of cells. For instance, many viruses, such as the potato leafroll virus, are limited to one host species or to one type of tissue within that species. A few viruses affect a broad range of hosts. An example of this is the rabies virus. Rabies can infect humans and many other animal hosts.

A virus cannot move by itself, but it can reach a host's body in several ways. For example, it can be carried onto a plant's surface by the wind or it can be inhaled by an animal. In a viral infection, the virus first attaches to the surface of the host cell. The virus and the place where it attaches must fit together exactly, as shown in **Figure 16.** Because of this, most viruses attack only one kind of host cell.

Viruses that infect bacteria are called bacteriophages (bak TIHR ee uh fay juhz). They differ from other kinds of viruses in the way that they enter bacteria and release their hereditary material. Bacteriophages attach to a bacterium and inject their hereditary material. The entire cycle takes about 20 min, and each virus-infected cell releases an average of 100 viruses.

Fighting Viruses

Vaccines are used to prevent disease. A vaccine is made from weakened virus particles that can't cause disease anymore. Vaccines have been made to prevent many diseases including measles, mumps, smallpox, chicken pox, polio, and rabies.

✔ **Reading Check** *What is a vaccine?*

The First Vaccine Edward Jenner is credited with developing the first vaccine in 1796. He developed a vaccine for smallpox, a disease that was still feared in the early twentieth century. Jenner noticed that people who got a disease called cowpox didn't get smallpox. He prepared a vaccine from the sores of people who had cowpox. When injected into healthy people, the cowpox vaccine protected them from smallpox. Jenner didn't know he was fighting a virus. At that time, no one understood what caused disease or how the body fought disease.

Treating and Preventing Viral Diseases Antibiotics are used to treat bacterial infections. They are ineffective against any viral disease. One way your body can stop viral infections is by making interferons. Interferons are proteins that protect cells from viruses. These proteins are produced rapidly by infected cells and move to noninfected cells in the host. They cause the noninfected cells to produce protective substances.

Antiviral drugs can be given to infected patients to help fight a virus. A few drugs show some effectiveness against viruses but some have limited use because of their adverse side effects.

Public health measures for preventing viral diseases include vaccinating people, improving sanitary conditions, quarantining patients, and controlling animals that spread the disease. Yellow fever was wiped out completely in the United States through mosquito-control programs. Annual rabies vaccinations protect humans by keeping pets and farm animals free from infection. To control the spread of rabies in wild animals such as coyotes and wolves, wildlife workers place bait containing an oral rabies vaccine, as shown in **Figure 17,** where wild animals will find it.

Research with Viruses

You might think viruses are always harmful. However, through research, scientists are discovering helpful uses for some viruses. One use, called gene therapy, is being tried on cells with defective genes. Normal hereditary material is substituted for a cell's defective hereditary material. The normal material is enclosed in viruses. The viruses then "infect" targeted cells, taking the new hereditary material into the cells to replace the defective hereditary material. Using gene therapy, scientists hope to help people with genetic disorders and find a cure for cancer.

Figure 17
This oral rabies bait is being prepared for an aerial drop by the Texas Department of Health as part of their Oral Rabies Vaccination Program. This five-year program has prevented the expansion of rabies into Texas.

Section 3 Assessment

1. Describe the structure of viruses and explain how viruses multiply.
2. How are vaccines beneficial?
3. How might some viruses be helpful?
4. How might viral diseases be prevented?
5. **Think Critically** Explain why a doctor might not give you any medication if you have a viral disease.

Skill Builder Activities

6. **Concept Mapping** Make an events chain concept map to show what happens when a latent virus becomes active. **For more help, refer to the** Science Skill Handbook.

7. **Using a Word Processor** Make an outline of the cycle of an active virus. **For more help, refer to the** Technology Skill Handbook.

Comparing Light Microscopes

You're a technician in a police forensic laboratory. You use a stereomicroscope and a compound light microscope in the laboratory. A detective just returned from a crime scene with bags of evidence. You must examine each piece of evidence under a microscope. How do you decide which microscope is the best tool to use?

Recognize the Problem

Will all of the evidence that you've collected be viewable through both microscopes?

Form a Hypothesis

Compare the items to be examined under the microscopes. Which microscope will be used for each item?

Possible Materials
compound light microscope
stereomicroscope
items from the classroom—include
   some living or once-living items (8)
microscope slides and coverslips
plastic petri dishes
distilled water
dropper

Goals
- **Learn** how to correctly use a stereomicroscope and a compound light microscope.
- **Compare** the uses of the stereomicroscope and compound light microscope.

Safety Precautions

Thoroughly wash your hands when you have completed this experiment.

Test Your Hypothesis

Plan

1. As a group, decide how you will test your hypothesis.

2. **Describe** how you will carry out this experiment using a series of specific steps. Make sure the steps are in a logical order. Remember that you must place an item in the bottom of a plastic petri dish to examine it under the stereomicroscope and you must make a wet mount of any item to be examined under the compound light microscope. For more help, see the Reference Handbook.

3. If you need a data table or an observation table, design one in your Science Journal.

Do

1. Make sure your teacher approves the objects you'll examine, your plan, and your data table before you start.

2. Carry out the experiment.

3. While doing the experiment, record your observations and complete the data table.

Analyze Your Data

1. **Compare** the items you examined with those of your classmates.

2. Based on this experiment, classify the eight items you observed.

Draw Conclusions

1. **Infer** which microscope a scientist might use to examine a blood sample, fibers, and live snails.

2. **List** five careers that require people to use a stereomicroscope. List five careers that require people to use a compound light microscope. Enter the lists in your Science Journal.

3. If you examined an item under a compound light microscope and a stereomicroscope, how would the images differ?

4. Which microscope was better for looking at large, or possibly live items?

*C*ommunicating Your Data

In your Science Journal, **write** a short description of an imaginary crime scene and the evidence found there. **Sort** the evidence into two lists—items to be examined under a stereomicroscope and items to be examined under a compound light microscope. **For more help, refer to the Science Skill Handbook.**

Magnification: 2,000×

This colored scanning electron micrograph (SEM) shows two breast cancer cells in the final stage of cell dvision.

Cobb Against Cancer

ew York City, 1950. Jewel Plummer put yet another slide onto the stage of her microscope and clipped it into place. She switched to the high power objective, looked through the eyepiece, and turned the fine adjustment a tiny bit to bring her subject—cells from a cancerous tumor—into focus. She switched back to low power and removed the slide. She had found no change in the tumor cells. The drug that doctors had used wasn't killing or slowing the growth rate of those cancer cells. Sighing, she reached for the next slide. Maybe the slightly different drug they had used on that batch of cells would be the answer....

Jewel Plummer Cobb is a cell biologist who did important background research on the use of drugs against cancer. She removed cells from cancerous tumors and cultured them in the lab. Then, in a controlled study, she tried a series of different drugs against batches of the same cells. Her goal was to find the right drug to cure each patient's particular cancer. Cobb never met that goal, but her research laid the groundwork for modern chemotherapy—the use of chemicals to treat people with cancer.

Role Model

Jewel Cobb also influenced the course of science in a different way. She served as dean or president of several universities, retiring as president of the University of California at Fullerton. In her role as a college official, she was able to promote equal opportunity for students of all backgrounds, especially in the sciences.

Light Up a Cure

Vancouver, British Columbia, 2000. While Cobb herself was only able to infer what was going on inside a cell from its reactions to various drugs, her work has helped others go farther. Building on Cobb's work, Professor Julia Levy and her research team at the University of British Columbia actually go inside cells and even inside organelles to work against cancer. One technique they are pioneering is the use of light to guide cancer drugs to the right cells. First, the patient is given a chemotherapy drug that reacts to light. Next, a fiber optic tube is inserted into the tumor. Finally, laser light is passed through the tube. The light activates the light-sensitive drug—but only in the tumor itself. This technique keeps healthy cells healthy but kills sick cells on the spot.

The image to the left shows human cervical cells magnified 125 times that have been attacked by cancer. The light blue areas at the center are keratin, a kind of protein. The cell nuclei are stained blue, and the red areas are fibroblasts, a kind of connective-tissue cell. These are the first human cells used to research cancer. This type of cell grows well in a lab, and is used in research worldwide.

CONNECTIONS Write Report on Cobb's experiments on cancer cells. What were her dependent and independent variables? What would she have used as a control? What sources of error did she have to guard against? Answer the same questions about Levy's work.

SCIENCE *Online*
For more information, visit science.glencoe.com

Chapter ② Study Guide

Reviewing Main Ideas

Section 1 Cell Structure

1. There are two basic cell types. Cells without membrane-bound structures are called prokaryotic cells. Cells with membrane-bound structures are called eukaryotic cells.

2. Most of the life processes of a cell occur within the cytoplasm.

3. Cell functions are performed by organelles under the control of DNA in the nucleus.

4. Organelles such as mitochondria and chloroplasts process energy.

5. Proteins take part in nearly every cell activity.

6. Golgi bodies and vacuoles transport substances, rid the cell of wastes, and store cellular materials. *What does this organelle do?*

7. Most many-celled organisms are organized into tissues, organs, and organ systems that perform specific functions to keep an organism alive.

Section 2 Viewing Cells

1. A simple microscope has just one lens. A compound light microscope has eyepiece lenses and objective lenses.

2. To calculate the magnification of a microscope, multiply the power of the eyepiece by the power of the objective lens.

3. An electron microscope uses a beam of electrons instead of light to produce an image of an object.

4. Things that are too small to be viewed with a light microscope can be viewed with an electron microscope. This is an SEM of an ant. *How do you know if the ant is alive or dead?*

5. According to the cell theory, the cell is the basic unit of life. Organisms are made of one or more cells, and all cells come from other cells.

Section 3 Viruses

1. A virus is a structure containing hereditary material surrounded by a protein coating.

2. A virus can make copies of itself only when it is inside a living host cell.

3. Viruses cause diseases in animals, plants, fungi, and bacteria. *Why don't scientists consider viruses like these in the photo to be living organisms?*

FOLDABLES
Reading & Study Skills

After You Read

On the inside of the Main Ideas Study Fold you made at the beginning of the chapter describe the characteristics of each type of cell.

Visualizing Main Ideas

Complete the following concept map of the basic units of life.

Vocabulary Review

Vocabulary Words

a. cell membrane
b. cell theory
c. cell wall
d. chloroplast
e. cytoplasm
f. endoplasmic reticulum
g. Golgi body
h. host cell
i. mitochondrion
j. nucleus
k. organ
l. organelle
m. ribosome
n. tissue
o. virus

THE PRINCETON REVIEW **Study Tip**

In order to understand the information that a graph is trying to communicate, write out a sentence that talks about the relationship between the *x*-axis and *y*-axis in the graph.

Using Vocabulary

Using the vocabulary words, give an example of each of the following.

1. found in every organ

2. smaller than one cell

3. a plant-cell organelle

4. part of every cell

5. organelle having a double membrane

6. used by biologists

7. contains hereditary material

8. a structure that surrounds the cell

9. can be damaged by a virus

10. made up of cells

Chapter 2 Assessment

Checking Concepts

Choose the word or phrase that best answers the question.

1. What structure allows only certain things to pass in and out of the cell?
   - **A)** cytoplasm
   - **C)** ribosomes
   - **B)** cell membrane
   - **D)** Golgi body

2. Which microscope uses lenses to magnify?
   - **A)** compound light microscope
   - **B)** scanning electron microscope
   - **C)** transmission electron microscope
   - **D)** atomic force microscope

3. What is made of folded membranes that move materials around inside the cell?
   - **A)** nucleus
   - **B)** cytoplasm
   - **C)** Golgi body
   - **D)** endoplasmic reticulum

4. Which scientist gave the name *cells* to structures he viewed?
   - **A)** Hooke
   - **C)** Schleiden
   - **B)** Schwann
   - **D)** Virchow

5. What organelle helps recycle old cell parts?
   - **A)** chloroplast
   - **C)** lysosome
   - **B)** centriole
   - **D)** cell wall

6. Which of the following is a viral disease?
   - **A)** tuberculosis
   - **C)** smallpox
   - **B)** anthrax
   - **D)** tetanus

7. What are structures in the cytoplasm of a eukaryotic cell called?
   - **A)** organs
   - **C)** organ systems
   - **B)** organelles
   - **D)** tissues

8. Which microscope magnifies up to a million times or more?
   - **A)** compound light microscope
   - **B)** stereomicroscope
   - **C)** transmission electron microscope
   - **D)** atomic force microscope

9. Which of the following is part of a bacterial cell?
   - **A)** a cell wall
   - **C)** mitochondria
   - **B)** lysosomes
   - **D)** a nucleus

10. Which of the following do groups of different tissues form?
   - **A)** organ
   - **C)** organ system
   - **B)** organelle
   - **D)** organism

Thinking Critically

11. Why is it difficult to treat a viral disease?

12. What type of microscope would be best to view a piece of moldy bread? Explain.

13. What would happen to a plant cell that suddenly lost its chloroplasts?

14. What would happen to this animal cell if it didn't have ribosomes?

15. How would you decide whether an unknown cell was an animal cell, a plant cell, or a bacterial cell?

Developing Skills

16. **Sequencing** Sequence the following from simple to complex: *small intestine, circular muscle cell, human,* and *digestive system.*

17. **Interpreting Scientific Illustrations** Use the illustrations in **Figure 1** to describe how the shape of a cell is related to its function.

18. **Making and Using Graphs** Use a computer to make a line graph of the following data. At 37°C there are 1.0 million viruses; at, 37.5°C, 0.5 million; at 37.8°C, 0.25 million; at 38.3°C, 0.1 million; and at 38.9°C, 0.05 million.

19. Comparing and Contrasting Complete the following table to compare and contrast the structures of a prokaryotic cell to those of a eukaryotic cell.

Cell Structures		
Structure	**Prokaryotic Cell**	**Eukaryotic Cell**
Cell Membrane		Yes
Cytoplasm	Yes	
Nucleus		Yes
Endoplasmic Reticulum		
Golgi Bodies		

20. Making a Model Make and illustrate a time line to show the development of the cell theory. Begin with the development of the microscope and end with Virchow. Include the contributions of Leeuwenhoek, Hooke, Schleiden, and Schwann.

Performance Assessment

21. Model Use materials that resemble cell parts or that represent their functions to make a model of a plant cell or an animal cell. Make a key to the cell parts to explain your model.

22. Poster Research the history of vaccinations. Contact your local Health Department for current information. Display your results on a poster.

TECHNOLOGY

Go to the Glencoe Science Web site at **science.glencoe.com** or use the **Glencoe Science CD-ROM** for additional chapter assessment.

THE PRINCETON REVIEW — Test Practice

A scientist is studying living cells. Below is an image of one of the cells that he is studying. This image represents what the scientist sees when he uses a tool in his laboratory.

Closely examine the image above then answer the following questions.

1. If the pointer shown above with the cell is 10 micrometers in length, then about how wide is this cell?
   A) 20 micrometers
   B) 10 micrometers
   C) 5 micrometers
   D) 0.1 micrometers

2. Which of the following tools is the scientist probably using to view the living cell?
   F) telescope
   G) endoplasmic reticulum
   H) compound light microscope
   J) kaleidoscope

Cell Processes

The Sun is hot. Your back aches and your hands are sore. Weeding a garden is hard work. You are sweaty, tired, thirsty, and hungry. Are the weeds having the same reactions? You may know that plants don't sweat or get tired, but they do need water and food, just like you. How do plants take in and use water and food? In this chapter you'll find the answer to this question. You'll also find out how living things get the energy that they need to survive.

What do you think?

Science Journal Look at the picture below with a classmate. Discuss what this might be or what is happening. Here's a hint: *It's sometimes called the powerhouse of the cell.* Write your answer or best guess in your Science Journal.

I f you forget to water a plant, it will wilt. After you water the plant, it probably will straighten up and look healthier. Why does the plant straighten? In the following activity, find out about water entering and leaving plant cells.

Demonstrate why water leaves plant cells

1. Label a small bowl "salt water." Pour 250 mL of water into the bowl. Then add 15 g of salt to the water and stir.

2. Pour 250 mL of water into another small bowl.

3. Place two carrot sticks into each bowl. Also, place two carrot sticks on the lab table.

4. After 30 min, remove the carrot sticks from the bowls and keep them next to the bowl they came from. Examine all six carrot sticks then describe them in your Science Journal.

Observe

Predict what would happen if you moved the carrot sticks from the plain water to the lab table, the ones from the salt water into the plain water, and the ones from the lab table into the salt water. Now try it. Write your predictions and your results in your Science Journal.

Before You Read

FOLDABLES
Reading & Study Skills

Making a Vocabulary Study Fold To help you study cell processes, make the following vocabulary Foldable. Knowing the definition of vocabulary words in a chapter is a good way to ensure you have understood the content.

1. Place a sheet of notebook paper in front of you so the short side is at the top. Fold the paper in half from the left to the right side.

2. Through the top thickness of paper, cut along every third line from the outside edge to the center fold, forming ten tabs as shown.

3. On the front of each tab, write a vocabulary word listed on the first page of each section in this chapter. On the back of each tab, define the word.

① Chemistry of Life

The Nature of Matter

Think about everything that surrounds you—chairs, books, clothing, other students, and air. What are all these things made up of? You're right if you answer "matter and energy." Matter is anything that has mass and takes up space. Energy is anything that brings about change. Everything in your environment, including you, is made of matter. Energy can hold matter together or break it apart. For example, the food you eat is matter that is held together by chemical energy. When food is cooked, energy in the form of heat can break some of the bonds holding the matter in food together. **Table 1** compares matter and energy and gives some examples of each.

Atoms Whether it is solid, liquid, or gas, matter is made of atoms. **Figure 1** shows a model of an oxygen atom. At the center of an atom is a nucleus that contains protons and neutrons. Although they have nearly equal masses, a proton has a positive charge and a neutron has no charge. Outside the nucleus are electrons, each of which has a negative charge. It takes about 1,837 electrons to equal the mass of one proton. Electrons are important because they are the part of the atom that is involved in chemical reactions. Look at **Figure 1** again and you will see that an atom is mostly empty space. Energy holds the parts of an atom together.

Figure 1
An oxygen atom model shows the placement of electrons, protons, and neutrons.

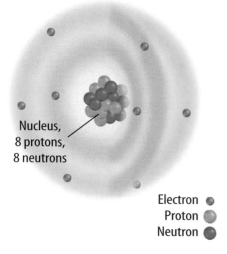

Oxygen atom

Nucleus,
8 protons,
8 neutrons

Electron ●
Proton ●
Neutron ●

Table 1	Matter and Energy	
	Definition	**Examples**
Matter	anything that has mass and takes up space	atoms, electrons, protons, and neutrons, living things, rocks, soil, and air
Energy	ability to cause change	sunlight, electricity, heat, chemical energy

Table 2 Elements That Make Up the Human Body		
Symbol	Element	Percent
O	Oxygen	65.0
C	Carbon	18.5
H	Hydrogen	9.5
N	Nitrogen	3.2
Ca	Calcium	1.5
P	Phosphorus	1.0
K	Potassium	0.4
S	Sulfur	0.3
Na	Sodium	0.2
Cl	Chlorine	0.2
Mg	Magnesium	0.1
	Other elements	0.1

Oxygen 65.0%

Carbon 18.5%

Hydrogen 9.5%

Nitrogen 3.2%

Calcium 1.5%

Phosphorus 1.0%
Other elements 1.3%

Elements When something is made up of only one kind of atom, it is called an element. An element can't be broken down into a simpler form by ordinary chemical reactions. The element oxygen is made up of only oxygen atoms, and hydrogen is made up of only hydrogen atoms. Scientists have given each element its own one- or two-letter symbol.

All elements are arranged in a chart known as the periodic table of elements. You can find this table at the back of this book. The table provides information about each element including its mass, how many protons it has, and its symbol.

Everything is made up of elements. Most things, including all living things, are made up of a combination of elements. Few things exist as pure elements. **Table 2** lists elements that are in the human body. What two elements make up most of your body?

✔ **Reading Check** *What types of things are made up of elements?*

Six of the elements listed in the table are important because they make up about 99 percent of living matter. The symbols for these elements are S, P, O, N, C, and H. Use **Table 2** to find the names of these elements.

Figure 2

The words *atoms, molecules,* and *compounds* are used to describe substances. *How are they related to each other?*

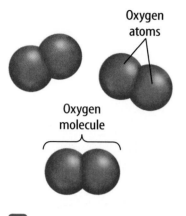

A Some elements, like oxygen, occur as molecules. These molecules contain atoms of the same element bonded together.

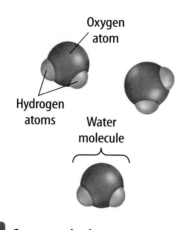

B Compounds also are composed of molecules. Molecules of compounds contain atoms of two or more different elements bonded together, as shown by these water molecules.

Compounds and Molecules

Suppose you make a pitcher of lemonade using a powdered mix and water. The water and the lemonade mix, which is mostly sugar, contain the elements oxygen and hydrogen. Yet, in one, they are part of a nearly tasteless liquid—water. In the other they are part of a sweet solid—sugar. How can the same elements be part of two materials that are so different? Water and sugar are compounds. Compounds are made up of two or more elements in exact proportions. For example, pure water, whether one milliliter of it or one million liters, is always made up of hydrogen atoms bonded to oxygen atoms in a ratio of two hydrogen atoms to one oxygen atom. Compounds have properties different from the elements they are made of. There are two types of compounds—molecular compounds and ionic compounds.

Molecular Compounds The smallest part of a molecular compound is a molecule. A molecule is a group of atoms held together by the energy of chemical bonds, as shown in **Figure 2.** When chemical reactions occur, chemical bonds break, new bonds form, and atoms are rearranged. The molecules produced are different from those that began the chemical reaction.

Molecular compounds form when different atoms share their outermost electrons. For example, two atoms of hydrogen can each share one electron with one atom of oxygen to form one molecule of water, as shown in **Figure 2B.** Water does not have the same properties as oxygen and hydrogen. Under normal conditions on Earth, oxygen and hydrogen are gases. Yet, water can be a liquid, a solid, or a gas. When hydrogen and oxygen combine, changes occur and a new substance forms.

Ions Atoms also combine because they've become positively or negatively charged. Atoms are usually neutral—they have no overall electric charge. When an atom loses an electron, it has more protons than electrons, so it becomes positively charged. When an atom gains an electron, it has more electrons than protons, so it becomes negatively charged. Electrically charged atoms—positive or negative—are called ions.

Ionic Compounds Ions of opposite charges attract one another to form electrically neutral compounds called ionic compounds. Table salt is made of sodium (Na) and chlorine (Cl) ions, as shown in **Figure 3.** When they combine, a chlorine atom gains an electron from a sodium atom. The chlorine becomes a negatively charged ion, and the sodium becomes a positively charged ion. These oppositely charged ions are attracted to each other and form the ionic compound sodium chloride, NaCl.

Ions are important in many life processes that take place in your body and in other organisms. For example, messages are sent along your nerves as potassium and sodium ions move in and out of nerve cells. Calcium ions are important in causing your muscles to contract. Ions also are involved in the transport of oxygen by your blood. The movement of some substances into and out of a cell would not be possible without ions.

Magnification: 8×

A Magnified crystals of salt look like this.

B The salt crystal is held together by the attraction between sodium ions and chlorine ions.

Figure 3
Table salt, or sodium chloride (NaCl), is a crystal composed of sodium ions and chlorine ions held together by ionic bonds.

Mixtures

Some substances, such as a combination of sugar and salt, can't change each other or combine chemically. A **mixture** is a combination of substances in which individual substances retain their own properties. Mixtures can be solids, liquids, gases, or any combination of them.

> ✔ **Reading Check** *Why is a combination of sugar and salt said to be a mixture?*

Most chemical reactions in living organisms take place in mixtures called solutions. You've probably noticed the taste of salt when you perspire. Sweat is a solution of salt and water. In a solution, two or more substances are mixed evenly. A cell's cytoplasm is a solution of dissolved molecules and ions.

Living things also contain mixtures called suspensions. A suspension is formed when a liquid or a gas has another substance evenly spread throughout it. Unlike solutions, the substances in a suspension eventually sink to the bottom. If blood, shown in **Figure 4,** is left undisturbed, the red blood cells and white blood cells will sink gradually to the bottom. However, the pumping action of your heart constantly moves your blood and the blood cells remain suspended.

Figure 4
When a test tube of whole blood is left standing, the blood cells sink in the watery plasma.

Table 3 Organic Compounds Found in Living Things

	Carbohydrate	Lipid	Protein	Nucleic Acid
Elements	carbon, hydrogen, and oxygen	carbon, oxygen, hydrogen, and phosphorus	carbon, oxygen, hydrogen, nitrogen, and sulfur	carbon, oxygen, hydrogen, nitrogen, and phosphorus
Examples	sugars, starch, and cellulose	fats, oils, waxes, phospholipids, and cholesterol	enzymes, skin, and hair	DNA and RNA
Function	supply energy for cell processes; form plant structures; short-term energy storage	store large amounts of energy long term; form boundaries around cells	regulate cell processes and build cell structures	carry hereditary information; used to make proteins

Organic Compounds

You and all living things are made up of compounds that are classified as organic or inorganic. Rocks and other nonliving things contain inorganic compounds, but most do not contain large amounts of organic compounds. **Organic compounds** always contain carbon and hydrogen and usually are associated with living things. One exception would be nonliving things that are products of living things. For example, coal contains organic compounds because it forms from dead and decaying plants. Organic molecules can contain hundreds or even thousands of atoms that can be arranged in many ways. **Table 3** compares the four groups of organic compounds that make up all living things—carbohydrates, lipids, proteins, and nucleic acids.

Carbohydrates Carbohydrates are organic molecules that supply energy for cell processes. Sugars and starches are carbohydrates that cells use for energy. Some carbohydrates also are important parts of cell structures. For example, a carbohydrate called cellulose is an important part of plant cells.

Lipids Another type of organic compound found in living things is a lipid. Lipids do not mix with water. Lipids such as fats and oils store and release even larger amounts of energy than carbohydrates do. One type of lipid, the phospholipid, is a major part of cell membranes.

SCIENCE *Online*

Research Air is a mixture of many things. Weather forecasts often include information about air quality. Visit the Glencoe Science Web site at **science.glencoe.com** for more information about air quality. In your Science Journal list some things that may be measured when testing air quality.

Proteins Organic compounds called proteins have many important functions in living organisms. They are made up of smaller molecules called amino acids. Proteins are the building blocks of many structures in organisms. Your muscles contain large amounts of protein. Proteins are scattered throughout cell membranes. Certain proteins called **enzymes** regulate nearly all chemical reactions in cells.

Nucleic Acids Large organic molecules that store important coded information in cells are called nucleic acids. One nucleic acid, deoxyribonucleic acid, or DNA—called genetic material—is found in all cells. It carries information that directs each cell's activities. Another nucleic acid, ribonucleic acid, or RNA, is needed to make enzymes and other proteins.

Inorganic Compounds

Most **inorganic compounds** are made from elements other than carbon. Generally, inorganic molecules contain fewer atoms than organic molecules. Inorganic compounds are the source for many elements needed by living things. For example, plants take up inorganic compounds from the soil. These inorganic compounds can contain the elements nitrogen, phosphorus, and sulfur. Many foods that you eat contain inorganic compounds. **Table 4** shows some of the inorganic compounds that are important to you. One of the most important inorganic compounds for living things is water.

Table 4 Some Inorganic Compounds Important in Humans	
Compound	**Use in Body**
Water	makes up most of the blood; most chemical reactions occur in water
Calcium phosphate	gives strength to bones
Hydrochloric acid	breaks down foods in the stomach
Sodium bicarbonate	helps the digestion of food to occur
Salts containing sodium, chlorine, and potassium	important in sending messages along nerves

Mini LAB

Determining How Enzymes Work

Procedure
1. Get two small cups of **prepared gelatin** from your teacher. Do not eat or drink anything in lab.
2. On the gelatin in one of the cups, place a piece of **fresh pineapple.**
3. Let both cups stand undisturbed during your class period. Wash your hands when you are done.
4. Observe what happens to the gelatin.

Analysis
1. What effect did the piece of fresh pineapple have on the gelatin?
2. What does fresh pineapple contain that caused it to have the effect on the gelatin you observed?
3. Why do the preparation directions on a box of gelatin dessert tell you not to mix it with fresh pineapple?

Importance of Water Some scientists hypothesize that life began in the water of Earth's ancient oceans. Chemical reactions may have occurred that produced organic molecules. Similar chemical reactions can take place in cells in your body.

Living things are composed of more than 50 percent water and depend on water to survive. You can live for weeks without food but only for a few days without water. **Figure 5** shows where water is found in your body. Although seeds and spores of plants, fungi, and bacteria can exist without water, they must have water if they are to grow and reproduce. All the chemical reactions in living things take place in water solutions, and most organisms use water to transport materials through their bodies. For example, many animals have blood that is mostly water to move materials. Plants use water to move minerals and sugars between the roots and leaves.

Math Skills Activity

Calculating the Importance of Water

All life on Earth depends on water for survival. Water is the most vital part of humans and other animals. It is required for all of the chemical processes that keep us alive.

Example Problem

At least 60% of an adult human body consists of water. If an adult man weighs 90 kg, how many kilograms of water does his body contain?

Solution

1 *This is what you know:*   adult human body = 60% water
                                                  man = 90 kg

2 *This is what you want to find:*   60% of 90 kg

3 *This is the equation you need to use:* $60/100 = x/90$

4 *Solve the equation for* x: $x = (60 \times 90)/100$
                                             $x = 54$ kg

Check your answer by dividing your answer by 90, then multiplying by 100. Do you get 60%?

Practice Problem

A human body at birth consists of 78% water. This percent gradually decreases to 60% in an adult. Assume a baby weighed 3.2 kg at birth, and grew into an adult weighing 95 kg. Calculate the approximate number of kilograms of water the human gained.

For more help, refer to the Math Skill Handbook.

Characteristics of Water

Physics INTEGRATION

The atoms of a water molecule are arranged in such a way that the molecule has areas with different charges. Water molecules are like magnets. Just like magnets have north and south poles that are attracted to each other, the positive part of one water molecule attracts the negative part of another water molecule, causing them to stick together. At the surface of water, molecules form a film. The film is strong enough to support small insects because the attraction between water molecules is greater than the attraction between the insect and gravity.

When heat is added to any substance, its molecules begin to move faster. Because water molecules are so strongly attracted to each other, water resists changes in temperature. The large percentage of water in living things acts like an insulator. The water in a cell helps to keep its temperature constant, which allows life-sustaining chemical reactions to take place.

You've seen ice floating on water. When water freezes, ice crystals form. In the crystals, each water molecule is spaced at a certain distance from all the others. Because this distance is greater in frozen water than in liquid water, ice floats on water. Bodies of water freeze from the top down. The floating ice provides insulation from extremely cold temperatures and allows living things to survive in the cold water under the ice.

Water outside of body cells ($33\frac{1}{3}$ %)

Water inside of body cells ($66\frac{2}{3}$ %)

Figure 5
About two thirds of your body's water is located within your body's cells. Water helps maintain the cells' shapes and sizes. One third of your body's water is outside of your body's cells.

Section 1 Assessment

1. What are the similarities and differences between atoms and molecules?
2. What is the difference between organic and inorganic compounds? Give an example of each type of compound.
3. What are the four types of organic compounds found in all living things?
4. Why does life as we know it depend on water?
5. **Think Critically** If you mix salt, sand, and sugar with water in a small jar, will the resulting mixture be a suspension, a solution, or both?

Skill Builder Activities

6. **Interpreting Scientific Illustrations** Carefully observe **Figure 1** and determine how many protons, neutrons, and electrons an atom of oxygen has. **For more help,** refer to the Science Skill Handbook.
7. **Using an Electronic Spreadsheet** Research to find the percentage of elements that make up Earth's crust. Make a spreadsheet that includes this information and the information in **Table 2.** Create a circle graph for each set of percentages. **For more help,** refer to the Technology Skill Handbook.

Moving Cellular Materials

As You Read

What You'll Learn

- **Describe** the function of a selectively permeable membrane.
- **Explain** how the processes of diffusion and osmosis move molecules in living cells.
- **Explain** how passive transport and active transport differ.

Vocabulary

passive transport	active transport
diffusion	endocytosis
equilibrium	exocytosis
osmosis	

Why It's Important

Cell membranes control the substances that enter and leave the cells in your body.

Passive Transport

"Close that window. Do you want to let in all the bugs and leaves?" How do you prevent unwanted things from coming through the window? As seen in **Figure 6,** a window screen provides the protection needed to keep unwanted things outside. It also allows some things to pass into or out of the room like air, unpleasant odors, or smoke.

Cells take in food, oxygen, and other substances from their environments. They also release waste materials into their environments. A cell has a membrane around it that works for a cell like a window screen does for a room. A cell's membrane is selectively permeable (PUR mee uh bul). It allows some things to enter or leave the cell while keeping other things outside or inside the cell. The window screen also is selectively permeable based on the size of its openings.

Things can pass through a cell membrane in several ways. Which way things move depends on the size of the molecules or particles, the path taken through the membrane, and whether or not energy is used. The movement of substances through the cell membrane without the use of energy is called **passive transport.** Cells use three types of passive transport. Which one is used depends on what is moving through the cell membrane.

Figure 6
A cell membrane, like a screen, will let some things through more easily than others. Air gets through a screen, but insects are kept out.

Figure 7
Like all other cells in your body, cells in your toes need oxygen.

B In your big toe, oxygen diffuses out of your red blood cells.

Air sac in lung

Oxygen

Red blood cell

A In your lungs, oxygen diffuses into your red blood cells.

Toe cell

Oxygen

Nucleus

Red blood cell

Diffusion Sometimes you can smell the scent of perfume when you sit near someone in a room, on a bus, or as you walk past him or her. When that happens, you are experiencing the effects of diffusion. When some molecules move away from areas where there are more of them into areas where there are fewer of them, it is called **diffusion.** Diffusion is one type of passive transport that takes place in cells. Molecules in solids, liquids, and gases constantly and randomly move. Random movement of molecules is why diffusion occurs. When the molecules of one substance are spread evenly throughout another substance, **equilibrium** occurs and diffusion stops. When equilibrium is reached, molecules continue to move and maintain equilibrium.

✔ Reading Check *What is equilibrium?*

Every cell in your body, including those in your big toe, needs oxygen. When you breathe, how does oxygen get from your lungs to cells in your big toe? Oxygen is carried throughout your body in your blood by the red blood cells. When your blood is pumped from your heart to your lungs, your red blood cells do not contain much oxygen. However, your lungs have more oxygen molecules than your red blood cells do, so the oxygen molecules diffuse into your red blood cells, as shown in **Figure 7A.** When the blood reaches your big toe, there are more oxygen molecules in your red blood cells than in your big toe cells. The oxygen diffuses out of your red blood cells and into your big toe cells, as shown in **Figure 7B.**

TRY AT HOME
Mini LAB

Observing Diffusion
Procedure 🥽 ♨ 🧤
1. Use **two clean glasses** of equal size. Label one "hot," then fill it until half full with **very warm water.** Label the other "cold," then fill it until half full with **cold water. WARNING:** *Do not use boiling hot water.*
2. Add one drop of **food coloring** to each glass. Carefully release the drop just at the water's surface to avoid splashing the water.
3. Observe the glasses. Record your observations immediately and again after 15 min.

Analysis
1. Describe what happens when food coloring is added to each glass.
2. How does temperature affect the rate of diffusion?

Osmosis—The Diffusion of Water Remember that water makes up a large part of living matter. Cells contain water and are surrounded by water. Water molecules move by diffusion into and out of cells. The diffusion of water through a cell membrane is called **osmosis.**

If cells weren't surrounded by water that contains few dissolved substances, water inside the cells would diffuse out of them. This is why water left the carrot cells in this chapter's Explore Activity. Because there were relatively fewer water molecules in the salt solution around the carrot cells than in the carrot cells, water moved out of the cells and into the salt solution.

Losing water from inside a plant cell causes the cell membrane to come away from the cell wall, as shown in **Figure 8A.** This reduces the pressure against the cell wall, and the plant cell becomes limp. If the carrot sticks were taken out of the salt water and put in pure water, the water around the cells would move into the cells. The cells would fill with water and their cell membranes would press against their cell walls, as shown in **Figure 8B.** Pressure would increase and the plant cells would become firm. That is why the carrot sticks would be crisp again.

 Reading Check *Why do carrots in salt water become limp?*

Osmosis also takes place in animal cells. If animal cells were placed in pure water, they too would swell up. However, animal cells have no cell walls. Just like an overfilled water balloon, they will burst if too much water enters the cell.

Figure 8
Cells respond to differences between the amount of water inside and outside the cell.

A The carrot stick becomes limp when more water leaves each of its cells than enters them.

B Equilibrium occurs when water leaves and enters the cells at the same rate.

Facilitated Diffusion Cells take in many substances. Some substances pass easily through the cell membrane by diffusion. Other substances, such as glucose molecules, are so large that they can enter the cell only with the help of molecules in the cell membrane called transport proteins. This process, a type of passive transport, is known as facilitated diffusion. Have you ever used the drive through at a fast-food restaurant to get your meal? The transport proteins in the cell membrane are like the drive-through window at the restaurant. The window lets you get food out of the restaurant and put money into the restaurant. Similarly, transport proteins are used to move substances into and out of the cell.

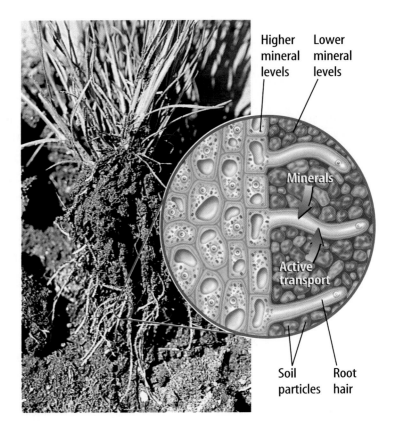

Higher mineral levels

Lower mineral levels

Minerals

Active transport

Soil particles

Root hair

Figure 9
Some root cells have extensions called root hairs that may be 5 mm to 8 mm long. Minerals are taken in by active transport through the cell membranes of root hairs.

Active Transport

Imagine that a football game is over and you leave the stadium. As soon as you get outside of the stadium, you remember that you left your jacket on your seat. Now you have to move against the crowd coming out of the stadium to get back in to get your jacket. Which required more energy—leaving the stadium with the crowd or going back to get your jacket? Something similar to this happens in cells.

Sometimes, a substance is needed inside a cell even though the amount of that substance inside the cell is already greater than the amount outside the cell. For example, root cells require minerals from the soil. The roots of the plant in **Figure 9** already may contain more of those mineral molecules than the surrounding soil does. The tendency is for mineral molecules to move out of the root by diffusion or facilitated diffusion. But the cell needs to move them back across the cell membrane and into the cell just like you had to move back into the stadium. To do this, energy is used. When energy is required to move materials through a cell membrane, **active transport** takes place.

Active transport involves transport proteins, just as facilitated diffusion does. In active transport, a transport protein binds with the needed particle and uses cellular energy to move it through the cell membrane. When the particle is released, the transport protein is ready to move another needed particle through the membrane.

Health
INTEGRATION

Transport proteins are important to your health. Sometimes transport proteins are missing or do not function correctly. What would happen if proteins that transport cholesterol across membranes were missing? Cholesterol is an important lipid used by your cells. Write your ideas in your Science Journal.

Endocytosis and Exocytosis

Some molecules and particles are too large to move by diffusion or to use the cell membrane's transport proteins. Large protein molecules and bacteria, for example, can enter a cell when they are surrounded by the cell membrane. The cell membrane folds in on itself, enclosing the item in a sphere called a vesicle. Vesicles are transport and storage structures in a cell's cytoplasm. The sphere pinches off, and the resulting vesicle enters the cytoplasm. A similar thing happens when you poke your finger into a partially inflated balloon. Your finger is surrounded by the balloon in much the same way that the protein molecule is surrounded by the cell membrane. This process of taking substances into a cell by surrounding it with the cell membrane is called **endocytosis** (en duh si TOH sus). Some one-celled organisms, as shown in **Figure 10,** take in food this way.

The contents of a vesicle may be released by the cell using a process called **exocytosis** (ek soh si TOH sus). Exocytosis occurs in the opposite way that endocytosis does. The membrane of the vesicle fuses with the cell's membrane, and the vesicle's contents are released. Cells in your stomach use this process to release chemicals that help digest food. The different ways that materials may enter or leave a cell are summarized in **Figure 11.**

Magnification: 1400×

Figure 10
One-celled organisms like this egg-shaped one can take in other one-celled organisms using endocytosis.

Section 2 Assessment

1. Explain how cell membranes are selectively permeable.
2. Compare and contrast the processes of osmosis and diffusion.
3. Identify the molecules that help substances move through the cell membrane during active transport and facilitated diffusion.
4. Why are endocytosis and exocytosis important processes to cells?
5. **Think Critically** Why are fresh fruits and vegetables sprinkled with water at produce markets?

Skill Builder Activities

6. **Concept Mapping** Make a network tree concept map to use as a study guide to help you tell the difference between passive transport and active transport. Begin with the phrase "Transport through membranes." **For more help, refer to the** Science Skill Handbook.

7. **Communicating** Seawater is saltier than tap water. In your Science Journal, explain why drinking large amounts of seawater would be dangerous to humans. **For more help, refer to the** Science Skill Handbook.

Figure 11

A flexible yet strong layer, the cell membrane is built of two layers of lipids (gold) pierced by protein "passageways" (purple). Molecules can enter or exit the cell by slipping between the lipids or through the protein passageways. Substances that cannot enter or exit the cell in these ways may be surrounded by the membrane and drawn into or expelled from the cell.

Diffusion and Osmosis

Facilitated Diffusion

Outside cell

Active Transport

Cell membrane

Inside cell

DIFFUSION AND OSMOSIS
Small molecules such as oxygen, carbon dioxide, and water can move between the lipids into or out of the cell.

FACILITATED DIFFUSION
Larger molecules such as glucose also diffuse through the membrane —but only with the help of transport proteins.

ACTIVE TRANSPORT
Cellular energy is used to move some molecules through protein passageways. The protein binds to the molecule on one side of the membrane and then releases the molecule on the other side.

ENDOCYTOSIS AND EXOCYTOSIS In endocytosis, part of the cell membrane wraps around a particle and engulfs it in a vesicle. During exocytosis, a vesicle filled with molecules bound for export moves to the cell membrane, fuses with it, and the contents are released to the outside.

Endocytosis

Exocytosis

Nucleolus   Nucleus

Activity

Observing Osmosis

It is difficult to see osmosis occurring in cells because most cells are so small. However, a few cells can be seen without the aid of a microscope. Try this activity to see how osmosis occurs in a large cell.

What You'll Investigate
How does osmosis occur in an egg cell?

Materials
unshelled egg	distilled water (250 mL)
balance	light corn syrup (250 mL)
spoon	500-mL container

Goals
- **Observe** osmosis in an egg cell.
- **Determine** what affects osmosis.

Safety Precautions

Eggs may contain bacteria. Avoid touching your face. Wash your hands thoroughly when you are done.

Procedure

1. Copy the table below into your Science Journal and use it to record your data.

Egg Mass Data
	Beginning Egg Mass	Egg Mass After Two Days
Distilled water		
Corn syrup		

2. Obtain an unshelled egg from your teacher. Handle the egg gently. Use a balance to find the egg's mass and record it in the table.

3. Place the egg in the container and add enough distilled water to cover it.

4. **Observe** the egg after 30 min, one day, and two days. After each observation, record the egg's appearance in your Science Journal.

5. After day two, remove the egg with a spoon and allow it to drain. Find the egg's mass and record it in the table.

6. Empty the container, then put the egg back in. Now add enough corn syrup to cover it. Repeat steps 4 and 5.

Conclude and Apply

1. **Explain** the difference between what happened to the egg in water and in corn syrup.

2. **Calculate** the mass of water that moved into and out of the egg.

3. **Hypothesize** why you used an unshelled egg for this investigation.

4. **Infer** what part of the egg controlled water's movement into and out of the egg.

Communicating Your Data

Compare your conclusions with those of other students in your class. **For more help, refer to the** Science Skill Handbook.

3 Energy for Life

Trapping and Using Energy

Think of all the energy that players use in a basketball game. Where does the energy come from? The simplest answer is "from the food they eat." The chemical energy stored in food is changed in cells into forms needed to perform all the activities necessary for life. In every cell, these changes involve chemical reactions. All of the activities of an organism involve chemical reactions in some way. The total of all chemical reactions in an organism is called **metabolism.**

The chemical reactions of metabolism need enzymes. What do enzymes do? Suppose you are hungry and decide to open a can of spaghetti. You use a can opener to open the can. Without a can opener, the spaghetti is unusable. The can of spaghetti changed because of the can opener, but the can opener did not change. The can opener can be used again later to open more cans of spaghetti. Enzymes in cells work something like can openers, as shown in **Figure 12.** The enzyme, like the can opener, causes a change, but it is not changed and is reusable. Unlike the can opener, which can only break things apart, enzymes also can cause molecules to join. Without the right enzymes, chemical reactions in cells cannot take place.

As You Read

What You'll Learn
- **List** the differences between producers and consumers.
- **Explain** how the processes of photosynthesis and respiration store and release energy.
- **Describe** how cells get energy from glucose through fermentation.

Vocabulary
metabolism respiration
photosynthesis fermentation

Why It's Important
Because of photosynthesis and respiration, you use the Sun's energy.

A   **B**

Enzyme   Enzyme

Large molecule   Small molecules

Figure 12
Enzymes are needed for most chemical reactions that take place in cells. **A** The enzyme attaches to the large molecule it will help change. **B** The enzyme causes the larger molecule to break down into two smaller molecules. Like the can opener, the enzyme is not changed and can be used again.

Photosynthesis
$$6CO_2 + 6H_2O + \text{light energy} \longrightarrow C_6H_{12}O_6 + 6O_2$$
carbon dioxide | water | chlorophyll | sugar | oxygen

Figure 13
Plants use photosynthesis to make food. *According to the chemical equation, what raw materials would the plant pictured need for photosynthesis?*

Photosynthesis Living things are divided into two groups—producers and consumers—based on how they obtain their food. Organisms that make their own food, such as plants, are called producers. Organisms that cannot make their own food are called consumers.

If you have ever walked barefoot across a sidewalk on a sunny summer day, you probably moved quickly because the sidewalk was hot. Sunlight energy was converted into thermal energy and heated the sidewalk. Plants and many other producers can convert sunlight energy into another kind of energy—chemical energy. The process they use is called photosynthesis. During **photosynthesis,** producers use light energy to make sugars, which can be used as food.

Producing Carbohydrates Producers that use photosynthesis are usually green because they contain a green pigment called chlorophyll (KLOR uh fihl). Chlorophyll and other pigments are used in photosynthesis to capture sunlight energy. In plant cells, these pigments are found in chloroplasts.

The captured sunlight energy is used to drive chemical reactions during which the raw materials, carbon dioxide and water, are used to produce sugar and oxygen. For plants, the raw materials come from air and soil. Some of the captured sunlight energy is stored in the chemical bonds that hold the sugar molecules together. **Figure 13** shows what happens during photosynthesis in a plant. Enzymes also are needed before these reactions can occur.

Storing Carbohydrates Plants make more sugar during photosynthesis than they need for survival. Excess sugar is changed and stored as starches or used to make other carbohydrates. Plants use these carbohydrates as food for growth, maintenance, and reproduction.

Why is photosynthesis important to consumers? Do you eat apples? Apple trees use photosynthesis to produce apples. Do you like cheese? Some cheese comes from milk, which is produced by cows that eat plants. Consumers take in food by eating producers or other consumers. No matter what you eat, photosynthesis was involved directly or indirectly in its production.

Respiration Imagine that you get up late for school. You dress quickly, then run three blocks to school. When you get to school, you feel hot and are breathing fast. Why? Your muscle cells need a lot of energy to help you run. To get this energy, muscle cells must break down food. Some of the energy from the food allows your muscles to move and some of it becomes thermal energy, which is why you get hot. Most cells also need oxygen to break down food. You were breathing fast because your body was working to get oxygen to your muscles. Your muscle cells were using the process of respiration. During **respiration** chemical reactions occur that break down food molecules into simpler substances and release their stored energy. Just as in photosynthesis, enzymes are needed before the chemical reactions of respiration can occur.

✓ Reading Check *What must happen to food molecules for respiration to take place?*

Breaking Down Carbohydrates The type of food that is most easily broken down by cells is carbohydrates. Respiration of carbohydrates begins in the cytoplasm of the cell. The carbohydrates are broken down into glucose molecules. Each glucose molecule is broken down further into two simpler molecules. As the glucose molecules are broken down, energy is released.

The two simpler molecules are broken down again. This breakdown occurs in the mitochondria of the cells of plants, animals, fungi, and many other organisms. This process uses oxygen, releases much more energy, and produces carbon dioxide and water as wastes. When you exhale, you breathe out carbon dioxide and some of the water.

Respiration occurs in the cells of all living things. **Figure 14** shows how respiration occurs in one consumer. As you are reading this section of the chapter, millions of cells in your body are breaking down glucose, releasing energy, and producing carbon dioxide and water.

Chemistry
INTEGRATION

Compounds often are represented by a chemical formula. The chemical formula shows how many and what type of atoms are found in one molecule of the compound. For example, the sugar glucose has the chemical formula $C_6H_{12}O_6$. What is the total number of atoms in one glucose molecule?

Figure 14
Producers and consumers use respiration to release energy from their foods.

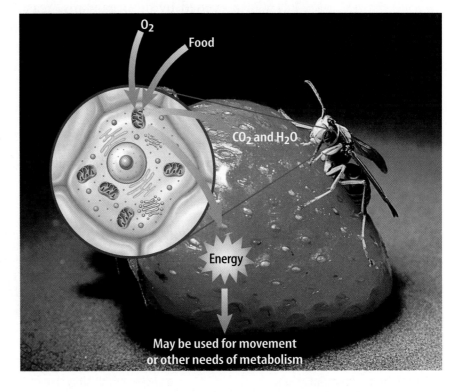

O$_2$
Food
CO$_2$ and H$_2$O
Energy
May be used for movement or other needs of metabolism

Fermentation Remember imagining you were late and had to run to school? During your run, your muscle cells might not have received enough oxygen, even though you were breathing rapidly. When cells do not have enough oxygen for respiration, they use a process called **fermentation** to release some of the energy stored in glucose molecules.

Like respiration, fermentation begins in the cytoplasm. Again, as the glucose molecules are broken down, energy is released. But, the simple molecules from the breakdown of glucose do not move into the mitochondria. Instead, more chemical reactions occur in the cytoplasm. These reactions release some energy and produce wastes. The wastes may be lactic acid, alcohol, and carbon dioxide, as shown in **Figure 15**. Your muscle cells can use fermentation to change the simple molecules into lactic acid while releasing energy. The presence of lactic acid is why your muscle cells might feel stiff and sore after you run to school.

✔ **Reading Check** *Where in a cell does fermentation take place?*

Some microscopic organisms, such as bacteria, carry out fermentation and make lactic acid. Some of these organisms are used to produce yogurt and some cheeses. These organisms break down a sugar in milk to release energy. The lactic acid produced causes the milk to become more solid and gives these foods some of their flavor.

Have you ever used yeast to make bread? Yeasts are one-celled living organisms. Yeast cells use fermentation to break down sugar in bread dough. They produce alcohol and carbon dioxide as wastes. The carbon dioxide waste is a gas that makes bread dough rise before it is baked. The alcohol is lost as the bread bakes.

Figure 15
Organisms that use fermentation produce several different wastes.

A Yeast cells produce carbon dioxide and alcohol as wastes when they use fermentation.

B Your muscle cells produce lactic acid as a waste when they use fermentation.

Figure 16
The chemical reactions of photosynthesis and respiration could not take place without each other.

Related Processes How are photosynthesis, respiration, and fermentation related? Some producers use photosynthesis to make food. All living things use respiration or fermentation to release energy stored in food. If you think carefully about what happens during photosynthesis and respiration, you will see that what is produced in one is used in the other, as shown in **Figure 16.** These two processes are almost the opposite of each other. Photosynthesis produces sugars and oxygen, and respiration uses these products. The carbon dioxide and water produced during respiration are used during photosynthesis. Most life would not be possible without these important chemical reactions.

Section 3 Assessment

1. Explain the difference between producers and consumers and give three examples of each.

2. Explain how the energy used by many living things on Earth can be traced back to sunlight.

3. Compare and contrast respiration and fermentation.

4. What condition must exist in cells for fermentation to occur?

5. **Think Critically** How can some indoor plants help improve the quality of air in a room?

Skill Builder Activities

6. **Identifying and Manipulating Variables and Controls** Design an experiment to show what happens to a plant when you limit sunlight or one of the raw materials for photosynthesis. Identify the control. **For more help, refer to the** Science Skill Handbook.

7. **Solving One-Step Equations** Refer to the chemical equation for photosynthesis. Calculate then compare the number of carbon, hydrogen, and oxygen atoms before and after photosynthesis. **For more help, refer to the** Math Skill Handbook.

Activity

Photosynthesis and Respiration

Every living cell carries on many chemical processes. Two important chemical processes are respiration and photosynthesis. All cells, including the ones in your body, carry on respiration. However, some plant cells can carry on both processes. In this experiment you will investigate when these processes occur in plant cells. How could you find out when plants were using these processes? Are the products of photosynthesis and respiration the same?

What You'll Investigate

When do plants carry on photosynthesis and respiration?

Materials

16-mm test tube (3)
150-mm test tube with stopper (4)
small, clear-glass baby food jar with lid (4)
test-tube rack
stirring rod
scissors
carbonated water (5 mL)
bromothymol blue solution in dropper bottle
aged tap water (20 mL)
distilled water (20 mL)
sprig of *Elodea* (2)
other water plants
Alternate materials

Goals

■ **Observe** green water plants in the light and dark.
■ **Determine** whether plants carry on photosynthesis and respiration.

Safety Precautions

Wear splash-proof safety goggles to protect eyes from hazardous chemicals. Wash hands thoroughly after the activity.

Procedure

1. Label each test tube using the numbers 1, 2, 3, and 4. Pour 5 mL of aged tap water into each test tube.

2. Add 10 drops of carbonated water to test tubes 1 and 2.

3. Add 10 drops of bromothymol blue to all of the test tubes. Bromothymol blue turns green to yellow in the presence of an acid.

4. Cut two 10-cm sprigs of *Elodea.* Place one sprig in test tube 1 and one sprig in test tube 3. Stopper all test tubes.

5. In your Science Journal, copy and complete the test-tube data table.

6. Place test tubes 1 and 2 in bright light. Place tubes 3 and 4 in the dark. Observe the test tubes for 30 min or until the color changes. Record the color of each of the four test tubes.

Test Tube Data		
Test Tube	Color at Start	Color After 30 Minutes
1		
2		
3		
4		

Conclude and Apply

1. What is indicated by the color of the water in all four test tubes at the start of the activity?

2. **Infer** what process occurred in the test tube or tubes that changed color after 30 min.

3. **Describe** the purpose of test tubes 2 and 4 in this experiment.

4. Do the results of this experiment show that photosynthesis and respiration occur in plants? Explain.

𝒞ommunicating Your Data

Choose one of the following activities to **communicate** your data. Prepare an oral presentation that explains how the experiment showed the differences between products of photosynthesis and respiration. Draw a cartoon strip to **explain** what you did in this experiment. Use each panel to show a different step. **For more help, refer to the Science Skill Handbook.**

"Tulip"
by Penny Harter

Respond to the Reading

1. Why do you suppose the tulip survived the builders' abuse?

2. The poet chooses to write about a tulip rather than another kind of flower. Why do you think that is?

3. What is the yellow throat that the narrator is staring into?

I watched its first green push
through bare dirt, where the builders
had dropped boards, shingles,
plaster—
killing everything.
I could not recall what grew
    there,
what returned each spring,
but the leaves looked tulip,
and one morning it arrived,
a scarlet slash against the
aluminum siding.

Mornings, on the way to
    my car,
I bow to the still bell
of its closed petals; evenings
it greets me, light ringing at
the end of my driveway.

Sometimes I kneel
to stare into the yellow
    throat . . .
It opens and closes my days.
It has made me weak with
    love. . . .

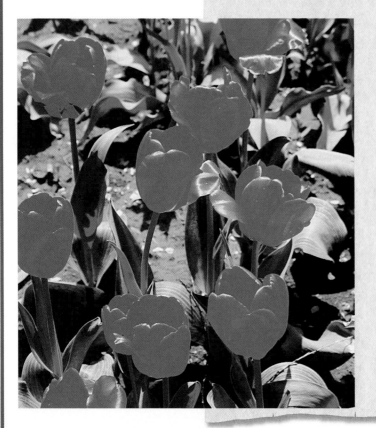

Understanding Literature

Personification Using human traits or emotions to describe an idea, animal, or inanimate object is called personification. When the poet writes that the tulip has a "yellow throat," she uses personification. This can make the reader think of the tulip as more than just an inanimate object. The poet also uses of personification when she states that the tulip inspires love.

Science Connection Living things are made of more than 50 percent water and depend on it for their survival. Because chemical reactions almost always require water to take place, plants must have water in order to grow. In the poem, the tulip only pushes up through the ground in the spring when the tulip's underground bulb and roots absorb enough water. The water carries nutrients and minerals from the soil into the plant.

The process of active transport allows needed nutrients to enter the roots. The cell membranes of root cells contain proteins that bind with the needed nutrients. Cellular energy is used to move these nutrients through the cell membrane.

You also learned about photosynthesis in this chapter. From reading the poem, how would you know that photosynthesis had taken place?

Linking Science and Writing

Gardener's Journal Select a plant to observe. It could be a plant that you, your family, or one of your classmates grows. Depending on the season, it could be a plant growing on the grounds of your school or in a public park. Keep a gardener's observation journal of the plant for a month. Write weekly entries in your journal, describing the plant's condition, size, health, color, and other physical qualities.

Career Connection

Microbiologist

Dr. Harold Amos is a biologist who has studied cell processes in bacteria and mammals over the course of his career. He studied the way that sugar is transported in normal cells and cancer cells. Dr. Amos has a medical degree and a doctorate in bacteriology and immunology, which deals with the immune system and its interaction with diseases. He also has received many awards for his scientific work and his contributions to the careers of other scientists.

SCIENCE*Online* Visit the Glencoe Science Web site at **science.glencoe.com** to learn more about careers in microbiology.

Chapter 3 Study Guide

Reviewing Main Ideas

Section 1 Chemistry of Life

1. Matter is anything that has mass and takes up space.

2. Energy in matter is in the chemical bonds that hold matter together.

3. All organic compounds contain the elements hydrogen and carbon. The organic compounds in living things are carbohydrates, lipids, proteins, and nucleic acids.

4. Organic and inorganic compounds are important to living things. *What organic compounds could be found in an elephant and a pumpkin?*

Section 2 Moving Cellular Materials

1. The selectively permeable cell membrane controls which molecules can pass into and out of the cell.

2. In diffusion, molecules move from areas where there are more of them into areas where there are fewer of them. Osmosis is the diffusion of water through a cell membrane. *Why might these plants use osmosis?*

3. Cells use energy to move molecules by active transport but do not use energy for passive transport.

4. Cells move large particles through cell membranes by endocytosis and exocytosis.

Section 3 Energy for Life

1. Photosynthesis is the process by which some producers change light energy into chemical energy. *Why can't cells in these humans use sunlight to make food?*

2. Respiration that uses oxygen releases the energy in food molecules and produces waste carbon dioxide and water.

3. Some one-celled organisms and cells that lack oxygen use fermentation to release small amounts of energy from glucose. Wastes like alcohol, carbon dioxide, and lactic acid are produced.

FOLDABLES
Reading & Study Skills

After You Read

Under each tab of your Vocabulary Study Fold, write a sentence about one of the cell processes using the vocabulary word on the tab.

Visualizing Main Ideas

Complete the following table on energy processes.

Energy Processes	Photosynthesis	Respiration	Fermentation
Energy Source		food (glucose)	food (glucose)
In plant and animal cells, occurs in			
Reactants are			
Products are			

Vocabulary Review

Vocabulary Words

a. active transport
b. diffusion
c. endocytosis
d. enzyme
e. equilibrium
f. exocytosis
g. fermentation
h. inorganic compound
i. metabolism
j. mixture
k. organic compound
l. osmosis
m. passive transport
n. photosynthesis
o. respiration

Using Vocabulary

Use what you know about the vocabulary words to answer the following questions.

1. What is the diffusion of water called?

2. What type of protein regulates nearly all chemical reactions in cells?

3. How do large food particles enter an amoeba?

4. What type of compound is water?

5. What process is used by producers to convert sunlight energy into chemical energy?

6. What type of compounds always contain carbon and hydrogen?

7. What process uses oxygen to break down glucose?

8. What is the total of all chemical reactions in an organism called?

THE PRINCETON REVIEW **Study Tip**

Make a note of anything you don't understand so that you'll remember to ask your teacher about it.

Chapter 3 Assessment

Chapter **3** Assessment

Checking Concepts

Choose the word or phrase that best answers the question.

1. What is it called when cells use energy to move molecules?
   A) diffusion
   C) active transport
   B) osmosis
   D) passive transport

2. How might bacteria be taken into cells?
   A) osmosis
   C) exocytosis
   B) endocytosis
   D) diffusion

3. What occurs when molecules are distributed evenly through a solid, liquid, or gas?
   A) equilibrium
   C) fermentation
   B) metabolism
   D) cellular respiration

4. Which of the following substances is an example of a carbohydrate?
   A) enzymes
   C) waxes
   B) sugars
   D) proteins

5. What is RNA an example of?
   A) carbon dioxide
   C) lipid
   B) water
   D) nucleic acid

6. What organic molecule stores the greatest amount of energy?
   A) carbohydrate
   C) lipid
   B) water
   D) nucleic acid

7. Which of these formulas is an example of an organic compound?
   A) $C_6H_{12}O_6$
   C) H_2O
   B) NO_2
   D) O_2

8. What are organisms that cannot make their own food called?
   A) biodegradables
   C) consumers
   B) producers
   D) enzymes

9. Which one of these cellular processes requires the presence of chlorophyll?
   A) fermentation
   C) respiration
   B) endocytosis
   D) photosynthesis

10. What kind of molecule is water?
    A) organic
    C) carbohydrate
    B) lipid
    D) inorganic

Thinking Critically

11. If you could place one red blood cell in distilled water, what would you see happen to the cell? Explain.

12. In snowy places, salt is used to melt ice on the roads. Explain what could happen to many roadside plants as a result.

13. Why does sugar dissolve faster in hot tea than in iced tea?

14. What would happen to the consumers in a lake if all the producers died?

15. Meat tenderizers contain protein enzymes. How do these enzymes affect meat?

Developing Skills

16. **Concept Mapping** Complete the events-chain concept map to sequence the following parts of matter from smallest to largest: *atom, electron,* and *compound.*

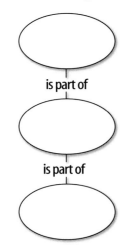

17. **Forming Hypotheses** Make a hypothesis about what will happen to wilted celery when placed in a glass of plain water.

18. Interpreting Data Water plants were placed at different distances from a light source. Bubbles coming from the plants were counted to measure the rate of photosynthesis. What can you say about how the distance from the light affected the rate?

Photosynthesis in Water Plants		
Beaker Number	Distance from Light (cm)	Bubbles per Minute
1	10	45
2	30	30
3	50	19
4	70	6
5	100	1

19. Making and Using Graphs Using the data from question 18, make a line graph that shows the relationship between the rate of photosynthesis and the distance from light.

Performance Assessment

20. Puzzle Make a crossword puzzle with words describing ways substances are transported across cell membranes. Use the following words in your puzzle: *diffusion, osmosis, facilitated diffusion, active transport, endocytosis,* and *exocytosis.* Make sure your clues give good descriptions of each transport method.

TECHNOLOGY

Go to the Glencoe Science Web site at **science.glencoe.com** or use the **Glencoe Science CD-ROM** for additional chapter assessment.

THE PRINCETON REVIEW **Test Practice**

Organic compounds called carbohydrates and proteins form many parts of a cell and also help connect cells to each other. Several organic compounds, along with their characteristics and where they are found, are listed below.

Cell Substances		
Organic Compound	Flexibility	Found In
Keratin	Not very flexible	Hair and skin of mammals
Collagen	Not very flexible	Skin, bones, and tendons of mammals
Chitin	Very rigid	Tough outer shell of insects, crabs
Cellulose	Very flexible	Trees and flowers

Study the chart and answer the following questions.

1. According to this information, which organic compound is the least flexible?
   A) keratin
   B) collagen
   C) chitin
   D) cellulose

2. According to the chart, cellulose might be found in _____.
   F) mammals
   G) bones
   H) insects
   J) trees

Cell Reproduction

How does a cut on your skin heal? Why doesn't a baby chicken grow up to look like a duck? Why do turtles, like the one in the photo to the right, and most other animals need to have two parents, when a sweet potato plant can be grown from just one potato? In this chapter, you will find answers to these questions as you learn about cell reproduction. You also will learn what genetic material is and how it functions.

What do you think?

Science Journal Look at the picture below with a classmate. Discuss what you think this might be. Here is a hint: *These structures contain important information for cells.* Write your answer or best guess in your Science Journal.

EXPLORE ACTIVITY

Most flower and vegetable seeds sprout and grow into entire plants in just a few weeks. Although all of the cells in a seed have information and instructions to produce a new plant, only some of the cells in the seed use the information. Where are these cells in seeds? Do the following activity to find out.

Infer about seed growth

1. Carefully split open two bean seeds that have soaked in water overnight.

2. Observe both halves and record your observations.

3. Wrap all four halves in a moist paper towel. Then put them into a self-sealing, plastic bag and seal the bag.

4. Make observations for a few days.

Observe

In your Science Journal, describe what you observe. Hypothesize about which cells in seeds use information about how plants grow.

Before You Read

FOLDABLES
Reading & Study
Skills

Making an Organizational Study Fold When information is grouped into clear categories, it is easier to make sense of what you are learning. Make the following Foldable to help you organize information about cell reproduction.

1. Place a sheet of paper in front of you so the long side is at the top. Fold the paper in half from the left side to the right side and then unfold.

2. Fold in each side to the center line to divide the paper into fourths.

3. Use a pencil to draw a cell on the front of your Foldable as shown.

4. As you read the chapter, use a pen to illustrate how the cell divides into two cells. Under the flaps, list how cells divide. In the middle section, list why cells divide.

Cell Division and Mitosis

As You Read

What You'll Learn

- **Explain** why mitosis is important.
- **Examine** the steps of mitosis.
- **Compare** mitosis in plant and animal cells.
- **List** two examples of asexual reproduction.

Vocabulary

mitosis
chromosome
asexual reproduction

Why It's Important

Your growth, like that of many organisms, depends on cell division.

Why is cell division important?

What do you, an octopus, and an oak tree have in common? You share many characteristics, but an important one is that you are all made of cells—trillions of cells. Where did all of those cells come from? As amazing as it might seem, many organisms, start as just one cell. That cell divides and becomes two, two become four, four become eight, and so on. Many-celled organisms, including you, grow because cell division increases the total number of cells in an organism. Even after growth stops, cell division is still important. Every day, billions of red blood cells in your body wear out and are replaced. During the few seconds it takes you to read this sentence, your bone marrow produced about six million red blood cells. Cell division is important to one-celled organisms, too—it's how they reproduce themselves, as shown in **Figure 1B.** Cell division isn't as simple as just cutting the cell in half, so how do cells divide?

The Cell Cycle

A living organism has a life cycle. A life cycle begins with the organism's formation, is followed by growth and development, and finally ends in death. Right now, you are in a stage of your life cycle called adolescence, which is a period of active growth and development. Individual cells also have life cycles.

Figure 1
All organisms use cell division.

A Many-celled organisms, such as this octopus, grow by increasing the numbers of their cells.

B A one-celled organism, such as this amoeba, reaches a certain size and then reproduces.

Figure 2
Interphase is the longest part of the cell cycle. *When do chromosomes duplicate?*

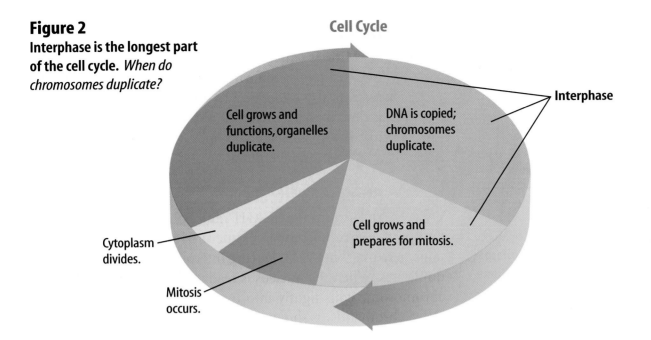

Cell Cycle

Cell grows and functions, organelles duplicate.

DNA is copied; chromosomes duplicate.

Interphase

Cell grows and prepares for mitosis.

Cytoplasm divides.

Mitosis occurs.

Length of Cycle The cell cycle, as shown in **Figure 2,** is a series of events that takes place from one cell division to the next. The time it takes to complete a cell cycle is not the same in all cells. For example, the cycle for cells in some bean plants takes about 19 h to complete. Cells in animal embryos divide rapidly and can complete their cycles is less than 20 min. In some human cells, the cell cycle takes about 16 h. Cells in humans that are needed for repair, growth, or replacement, like skin and bone cells, constantly repeat the cycle.

Interphase Most of the life of any eukaryotic cell—a cell with a nucleus—is spent in a period of growth and development called interphase. Cells in your body that no longer divide, such as nerve and muscle cells, are always in interphase. An actively dividing cell, such as a skin cell, copies its hereditary material and prepares for cell division during interphase.

Why is it important for a cell to copy its hereditary information before dividing? Imagine that you have a part in a play and the director has one complete copy of the script. If the director gave only one page to each person in the play, no one would have the entire script. Instead the director makes a complete, separate copy of the script for each member of the cast so that each one can learn his or her part. Before a cell divides, a copy of the hereditary material must be made so that each of the two new cells will get a complete copy. Just as the actors in the play need the entire script, each cell needs a complete set of hereditary material to carry out life functions.

After interphase, cell division begins. The nucleus divides, and then the cytoplasm separates to form two new cells.

A Duplication **B** Chromatids

Centromere

Unduplicated chromosome

Duplicated chromosome

Figure 3
DNA is copied during interphase. **A** An unduplicated chromosome has one strand of DNA. **B** A duplicated chromosome has two identical DNA strands, called chromatids, that are held together at a region called the centromere.

Figure 4
The cell plate shown in this plant cell appears when the cytoplasm is being divided.

Cell plate

Mitosis

Mitosis (mi TOH sus) is the process in which the nucleus divides to form two identical nuclei. Each new nucleus also is identical to the original nucleus. Mitosis is described as a series of phases, or steps. The steps of mitosis in order are named prophase, metaphase, anaphase, and telophase.

Steps of Mitosis When any nucleus divides, the chromosomes (KROH muh sohmz) play the important part. A **chromosome** is a structure in the nucleus that contains hereditary material. During interphase, each chromosome duplicates. When the nucleus is ready to divide, each duplicated chromosome coils tightly into two thickened, identical strands called chromatids, as shown in **Figure 3.**

✔ **Reading Check** *How are chromosomes and chromatids related?*

During prophase, the pairs of chromatids are fully visible when viewed under a microscope. The nucleolus and the nuclear membrane disintegrate. Two small structures called centrioles (SEN tree olz) move to opposite ends of the cell. Between the centrioles, threadlike spindle fibers begin to stretch across the cell. Plant cells also form spindle fibers during mitosis but do not have centrioles.

In metaphase, the pairs of chromatids line up across the center of the cell. The centromere of each pair usually becomes attached to two spindle fibers—one from each side of the cell.

In anaphase, each centromere divides and the spindle fibers shorten. Each pair of chromatids separates, and chromatids begin to move to opposite ends of the cell. The separated chromatids are now called chromosomes. In the final step, telophase, spindle fibers start to disappear the chromosomes start to uncoil, and a new nucleus forms.

Division of the Cytoplasm For most cells, after the nucleus has divided, the cytoplasm separates and two new cells are formed. In animal cells, the cell membrane pinches in the middle, like a balloon with a string tightened around it, and the cytoplasm divides. In plant cells, the appearance of a cell plate, as shown in **Figure 4,** tells you that the cytoplasm is being divided. New cell walls form along the cell plate, and new cell membranes develop inside the cell walls. Following division of the cytoplasm, most new cells begin the period of growth, or interphase, again. Review cell division for an animal cell using the illustrations in **Figure 5.**

Figure 5

Cell division for an animal cell is shown here. Each micrograph shown in this figure is magnified 600 times.

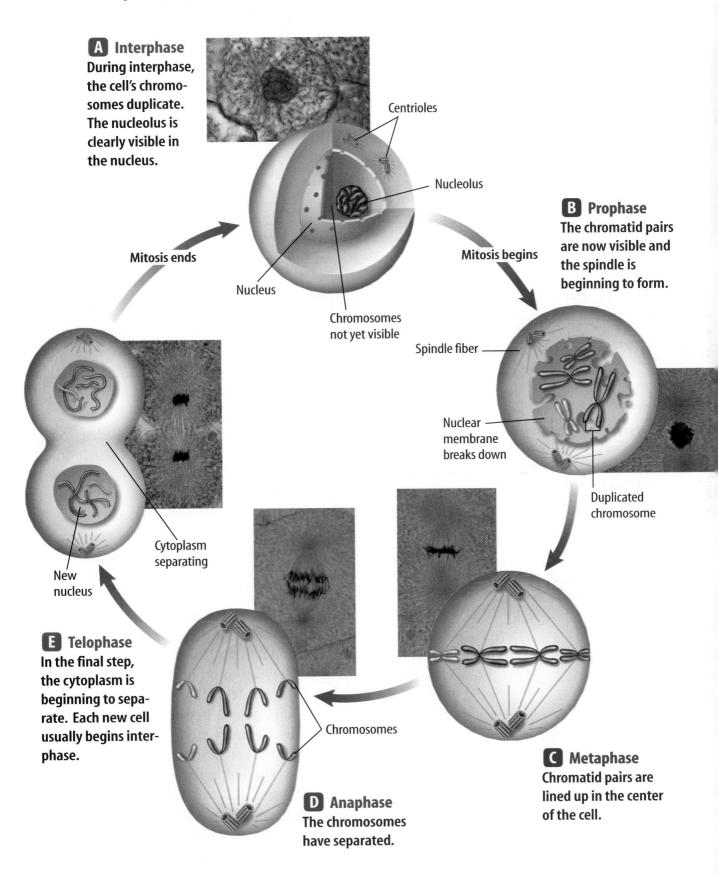

A Interphase
During interphase, the cell's chromosomes duplicate. The nucleolus is clearly visible in the nucleus.

Centrioles

Nucleolus

Nucleus

Chromosomes not yet visible

Mitosis ends

Mitosis begins

B Prophase
The chromatid pairs are now visible and the spindle is beginning to form.

Spindle fiber

Nuclear membrane breaks down

Duplicated chromosome

New nucleus

Cytoplasm separating

E Telophase
In the final step, the cytoplasm is beginning to separate. Each new cell usually begins interphase.

Chromosomes

D Anaphase
The chromosomes have separated.

C Metaphase
Chromatid pairs are lined up in the center of the cell.

Figure 6
Pairs of chromosomes are found in the nucleus of most cells.
A Most human cells have 23 pairs of chromosomes including one pair of chromosomes that help determine sex such as the XY in pair 23 above. **B** Most fruit fly cells have four pairs of chromosomes. *What do you think the XX pair in fruit flies helps determine?*

Results of Mitosis You should remember two important things about mitosis. First, it is the division of a nucleus. Second, it produces two new nuclei that are identical to each other and the original nucleus. Each new nucleus has the same number and type of chromosomes. Every cell in your body, except sex cells, has a nucleus with 46 chromosomes—23 pairs. This is because you began as one cell with 46 chromosomes in its nucleus. Skin cells, produced to replace or repair your skin have the same 46 chromosomes as the original single cell you developed from. Each cell in a fruit fly has eight chromosomes, so each new cell produced by mitosis has a copy of those eight chromosomes. **Figure 6** shows the chromosomes found in most human cells and those found in most fruit fly cells.

Each of the trillions of cells in your body, except sex cells, has a copy of the same hereditary material. Even though all actors in a play have copies of the same script, they do not learn the same lines. Likewise, all of your cells use different parts of the same hereditary material to become different types of cells.

Cell division allows growth and replaces worn out or damaged cells. You are much larger and have more cells than a baby mainly because of cell division. If you cut yourself, the wound heals because cell division replaces damaged cells. Another way some organisms use cell division is to produce new organisms.

Asexual Reproduction

Reproduction is the process by which an organism produces others of its same kind. Among living organisms, there are two types of reproduction—sexual and asexual. Sexual reproduction usually requires two organisms. In **asexual reproduction,** a new organism (sometimes more than one) is produced from one organism. The new organism will have hereditary material identical to the hereditary material of the parent organism.

> ✔ **Reading Check** *How many organisms are needed for asexual reproduction?*

Cellular Asexual Reproduction Organisms with eukaryotic cells asexually reproduce by cell division. A sweet potato growing in a jar of water is an example of asexual reproduction. All the stems, leaves, and roots that grow from the sweet potato have been produced by cell division and have the same hereditary material. New strawberry plants can be reproduced asexually from horizontal stems called runners. **Figure 7** shows asexual reproduction in a potato and a strawberry plant.

Recall that mitosis is the division of a nucleus. However, bacteria do not have a nucleus so they can't use mitosis. Instead, bacteria reproduce asexually by fission. During fission, an organism whose cells do not contain a nucleus copies its genetic material and then divides into two identical organisms.

Mini LAB

Modeling Mitosis

Procedure
1. Make models of cell division using **materials supplied by your teacher.**
2. Use four chromosomes in your model.
3. When finished, arrange the models in the order in which mitosis occurs.

Analysis
1. In which steps is the nucleus visible?
2. How many cells does a dividing cell form?

Figure 7
Many plants can reproduce asexually.

🅐 **A new potato plant can grow from each sprout on this potato.**

🅑 *How does the genetic material in the small strawberry plant compare to the genetic material in the large strawberry plant?*

Figure 8
Some organisms use mitosis for budding and regeneration.

B Some sea stars reproduce asexually by shedding arms. Each arm can grow into a new sea star.

A Hydra, a freshwater animal, can reproduce asexually by budding. The bud is a small exact copy of the adult.

Budding and Regeneration Look at **Figure 8A.** A new organism is growing from the body of the parent organism. This organism, called a hydra, is reproducing by budding. Budding is a type of asexual reproduction made possible because of cell division. When the bud on the adult becomes large enough, it breaks away to live on its own.

Could you grow a new finger? Some organisms can regrow damaged or lost body parts, as shown in **Figure 8B.** Regeneration is the process that uses cell division to regrow body parts. Sponges, planaria, sea stars, and some other organisms can use regeneration for asexual reproduction. If these organisms break into pieces, a whole new organism will grow from each piece. Because sea stars eat oysters, oyster farmers dislike them. What would happen if an oyster farmer collected sea stars, cut them into pieces, and threw them back into the ocean?

Section ① Assessment

1. What is mitosis and how does it differ in plants and animals?
2. Give two examples of asexual reproduction in many-celled organisms.
3. What happens to chromosomes before mitosis begins?
4. After a cell undergoes mitosis, how are the two new cells alike?
5. **Think Critically** Why is it important for the nuclear membrane to disintegrate during mitosis?

Skill Builder Activities

6. **Testing a Hypothesis** A piece of leaf, stem, or root can grow into a new plant. Hypothesize how you would use one of these plant parts to grow a new plant. Test your idea. **For more help, refer to the** Science Skill Handbook.
7. **Solving One-Step Equations** If a cell undergoes cell division every 5 min, how many cells will there be after 1 h? Calculate and record the answer in your Science Journal. **For more help, refer to the** Math Skill Handbook.

Activity

Mitosis in Plant Cells

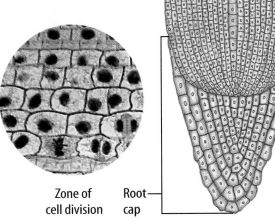

Reproduction of most cells in plants and animals uses mitosis and cell division. In this activity, you will study mitosis in plant cells by examining prepared slides of onion root-tip cells.

What You'll Investigate

How can plant cells in different stages of mitosis be distinguished from each other?

Materials

prepared slide of an onion root tip
microscope

Goals

- **Compare** cells in different stages of mitosis and observe the location of their chromosomes.
- **Observe** what stage of mitosis is most common in onion root tips.

Safety Precautions 🔬 🧤

Procedure

1. Copy the data table in your Science Journal.
2. **Obtain** a prepared slide of cells from an onion root tip.
3. Set your microscope on low power and examine the onion root tip. Move the slide until you can see the tip of the root. You will see several large round cells. These cells are called the root cap. Move your slide until you see the cells in the area just behind the root cap. Turn the nosepiece to high power.
4. Find one area of cells where you can see the most stages of mitosis. Count how many cells you see in each stage and record your data in the table.
5. Turn the microscope back to low power. Remove the onion root-tip slide.

Zone of cell division   Root cap

Conclude and Apply

1. **Compare** the cells in the region behind the root cap to those in the root cap.
2. **Calculate** the percent of cells found in each stage of mitosis. Infer which stage of mitosis takes the longest period of time.

Number of Root-Tip Cells Observed		
Stage of Mitosis	**Number of Cells Observed**	**Percent of Cells Observed**
Prophase		
Metaphase		
Anaphase		
Telophase		
Total		

Communicating Your Data

Write a story as if you were a cell in an onion root tip. Describe what changes occur as you go through mitosis. Use some of your drawings to illustrate the story. Share your story with your class. **For more help, refer to the Science Skill Handbook.**

Sexual Reproduction and Meiosis

Sexual Reproduction

Sexual reproduction is another way that a new organism can be produced. During **sexual reproduction,** two sex cells, sometimes called an egg and a sperm, come together. Sex cells, like those in **Figure 9,** are formed from cells in reproductive organs. **Sperm** are formed in the male reproductive organs. **Eggs** are formed in the female reproductive organs. The joining of an egg and a sperm is called **fertilization,** and the cell that forms is called a **zygote** (ZI goht). Generally, the egg and the sperm come from two different organisms of the same species. Following fertilization, mitosis begins. A new organism with a unique identity develops.

Diploid Cells   Your body forms two types of cells—body cells and sex cells. Body cells far outnumber sex cells. Your brain, skin, bones, and other tissues and organs are formed from body cells. A typical human body cell has 46 chromosomes. Each chromosome has a mate that is similar to it in size and shape and has similar DNA. Human body cells have 23 pairs of chromosomes. When cells have pairs of similar chromosomes, they are said to be **diploid** (DIH ployd).

Figure 9
A human sperm or egg cell contains only 23 chromosomes.

Human egg and many sperm

Magnification: 790×

Haploid Cells Because sex cells do not have pairs of chromosomes, they are said to be **haploid** (HA ployd). They have only half the number of chromosomes as body cells. *Haploid* means "single form." Human sex cells have only 23 chromosomes—one from each of the 23 pairs of similar chromosomes. Compare the chromosomes found in a sex cell, as shown in **Figure 9,** to the full set of human chromosomes seen in **Figure 6A.**

✔**Reading Check** *How many chromosomes are usually in each human sperm?*

Meiosis and Sex Cells

A process called **meiosis** (mi OH sus) produces haploid sex cells. What would happen in sexual reproduction if two diploid cells combined? The offspring would have twice as many chromosomes as its parent. Although plants with twice the number of chromosomes are often produced, most animals would not survive with a double number of chromosomes. Meiosis ensures that the offspring will have the same diploid number as its parent, as shown in **Figure 10.** After two haploid sex cells combine, a diploid zygote is produced that develops into a new diploid organism.

During meiosis, two divisions of the nucleus occur. These divisions are called meiosis I and meiosis II. The steps of each division have names like those in mitosis and are numbered for the division in which they occur.

Chemistry
INTEGRATION

The human egg releases a chemical into the surrounding fluid that attracts sperm. Usually, only one sperm fertilizes the egg. After the sperm nucleus enters the egg, the cell membrane of the egg changes in a way that prevents other sperm from entering. What adaptation in this process guarantees that the zygote will be diploid? Write a paragraph describing your ideas in your Science Journal.

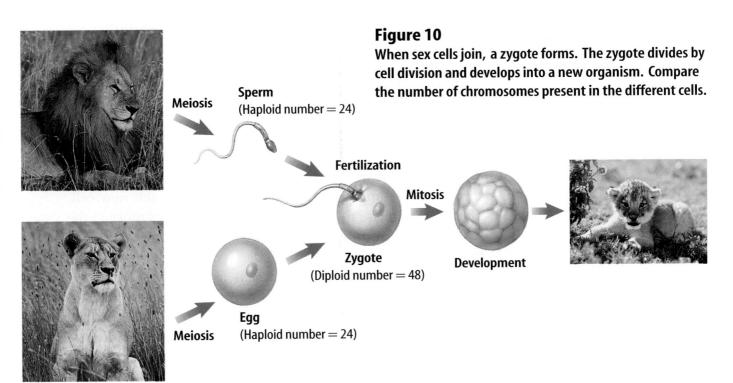

Figure 10
When sex cells join, a zygote forms. The zygote divides by cell division and develops into a new organism. Compare the number of chromosomes present in the different cells.

Meiosis
Sperm
(Haploid number = 24)

Fertilization

Mitosis

Zygote
(Diploid number = 48)

Development

Egg
(Haploid number = 24)

Meiosis

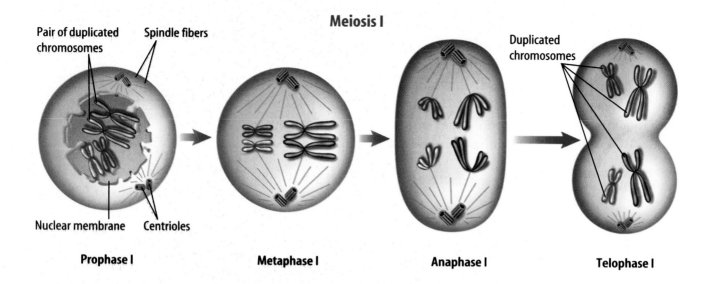

Meiosis I

Pair of duplicated chromosomes   Spindle fibers

Duplicated chromosomes

Nuclear membrane   Centrioles

Prophase I   Metaphase I   Anaphase I   Telophase I

Figure 11
Meiosis has two divisions of the nucleus—meiosis I and meiosis II. *How many sex cells are finally formed after both divisions are completed?*

Meiosis I Before meiosis begins, each chromosome is duplicated, just as in mitosis. When the cell is ready for meiosis, each duplicated chromosome is visible under the microscope as two chromatids. As shown in **Figure 11,** the events of prophase I are similar to those of prophase in mitosis. In meiosis, each duplicated chromosome comes near its similar duplicated mate. In mitosis they do not come near each other.

In metaphase I, the pairs of duplicated chromosomes line up in the center of the cell. The centromere of each chromatid pair becomes attached to one spindle fiber so, the chromatids do not separate in anaphase I. The two pairs of chromatids of each similar pair move away from each other to opposite ends of the cell. Each duplicated chromosome still has two chromatids. Then, in telophase I, the cytoplasm divides, and two new cells form. Each new cell has one duplicated chromosome from each similar pair.

Reading Check   *What happens to duplicated chromosomes during anaphase I?*

Meiosis II The two cells formed during meiosis I now begin meiosis II. The chromatids of each duplicated chromosome will be separated during this division. In prophase II, the duplicated chromosomes and spindle fibers reappear in each new cell. Then in metaphase II, the duplicated chromosomes move to the center of the cell. Unlike what occurs in metaphase I, each centromere now attaches to two spindle fibers instead of one. The centromere divides during anaphase II, and the chromatids separate and move to opposite ends of the cell. Each chromatid now is an individual chromosome. As telophase II begins, the spindle fibers disappear, and a nuclear membrane forms around the chromosomes at each end of the cell. When meiosis II is finished, the cytoplasm divides.

Meiosis II

Prophase II   Metaphase II   Anaphase II   Telophase II

Unduplicated chromosomes

Summary of Meiosis Two cells form during meiosis I. In meiosis II, both of these cells form two cells. The two divisions of the nucleus result in four sex cells, each has one-half the number of chromosomes in its nucleus that was in the original nucleus. From a human cell with 46 paired chromosomes, meiosis produces four sex cells each with 23 unpaired chromosomes.

Problem-Solving Activity

How can chromosome numbers be predicted?

Offspring get half of their chromosomes from one parent and half from the other. What happens if each parent has a different diploid number of chromosomes?

Identifying the Problem

A zebra and a donkey can mate to produce a zonkey. Zebras have a diploid number of 46. Donkeys have a diploid number of 60.

Solving the Problem

1. How many chromosomes would the zonkey receive from each parent?
2. What is the chromosome number of the zonkey?
3. What would happen when meiosis occurs in the zonkey's reproductive organs?
4. Predict why zonkeys are usually sterile.

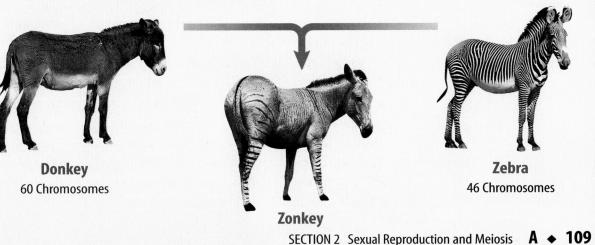

Donkey
60 Chromosomes

Zonkey

Zebra
46 Chromosomes

Figure 12

You received a haploid (n) set of chromosomes from each of your parents, making you a diploid (2n) organism. In nature, however, many plants are polyploid—they have three (3n), four (4n), or more sets of chromosomes. We depend on some of these plants for food.

▲ TRIPLOID Bright yellow bananas typically come from triploid (3n) banana plants. Plants with an odd number of chromosome sets usually cannot reproduce sexually and have very small seeds or none at all.

▲ TETRAPLOID Polyploidy occurs naturally in many plants—including peanuts and daylilies—due to mistakes in mitosis or meiosis.

▼ HEXAPLOID Modern cultivated strains of oats have six sets of chromosomes, making them hexaploid (6n) plants.

▲ OCTAPLOID Polyploid plants often are bigger than nonpolyploid plants and may have especially large leaves, flowers, or fruits. Strawberries are an example of octaploid (8n) plants.

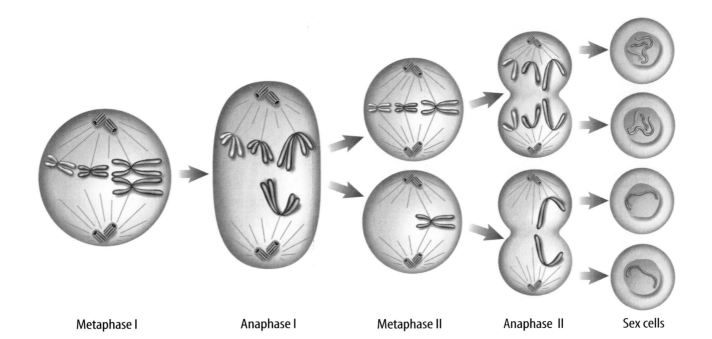

| Metaphase I | Anaphase I | Metaphase II | Anaphase II | Sex cells |

Mistakes in Meiosis Meiosis occurs many times in reproductive organs. Although mistakes in plants, as shown in **Figure 12,** are common, mistakes are less common in animals. These mistakes can produce sex cells with too many or too few chromosomes, as shown in **Figure 13.** Sometimes, zygotes produced from these sex cells die. If the zygote lives, every cell in the organism that grows from that zygote usually will have the wrong number of chromosomes. Organisms with the wrong number of chromosomes may not grow normally.

Figure 13
This diploid cell has four chromosomes. During anaphase I, one pair of duplicated chromosomes did not separate. *How many chromosomes does each sex cell usually have?*

Section 2 Assessment

1. Compare and contrast sexual and asexual reproduction.

2. What is a zygote, and how is it formed?

3. Give two examples of sex cells. Where are sex cells formed?

4. Compare what happens to chromosomes during anaphase I and anaphase II.

5. **Think Critically** Plants grown from runners and leaf cuttings have the same traits as the parent plant. Plants grown from seeds can vary from the parent plants in many ways. Suggest an explanation for why this can happen.

Skill Builder Activities

6. **Making and Using Tables** Make a table to compare mitosis and meiosis in humans. Vertical headings should include: *What Type of Cell (Body or Sex), Beginning Cell (Haploid or Diploid), Number of Cells Produced, End-Product Cell (Haploid or Diploid),* and *Number of Chromosomes in Cells Produced.* **For more help, refer to the** Science Skill Handbook.

7. **Communicating** Write a poem, song, or another memory device to help you remember the steps and outcome of meiosis. **For more help, refer to the** Science Skill Handbook.

③ DNA

As You Read

What You'll Learn

- **Identify** the parts of a DNA molecule and its structure.
- **Explain** how DNA copies itself.
- **Describe** the structure and function of each kind of RNA.

Vocabulary

DNA   RNA
gene   mutation

Why It's Important

DNA helps determine nearly everything your body is and does.

What is DNA?

Why was the alphabet one of the first things you learned when you started school? Letters are a code that you need to know before you learn to read. A cell also uses a code that is stored in its hereditary material. The code is a chemical called deoxyribonucleic (dee AHK sih ri boh noo klay ihk) acid, or **DNA.** It contains information for an organism's growth and function. **Figure 14** shows how DNA is stored in cells that have a nucleus. When a cell divides, the DNA code is copied and passed to the new cells. In this way, new cells receive the same coded information that was in the original cell. Every cell that has ever been formed in your body or in any other organism contains DNA.

Chemistry INTEGRATION

Discovering DNA Since the mid-1800s, scientists have known that the nuclei of cells contain large molecules called nucleic acids. By 1950, chemists had learned what the nucleic acid DNA was made of, but they didn't understand how the parts of DNA were arranged.

Figure 14
DNA is part of the chromosomes found in a cell's nucleus.

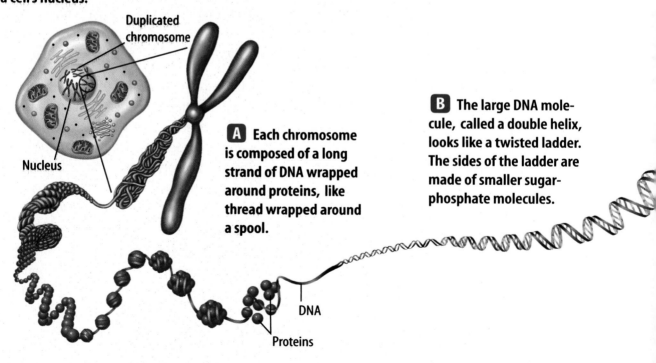

Duplicated chromosome

Nucleus

A Each chromosome is composed of a long strand of DNA wrapped around proteins, like thread wrapped around a spool.

B The large DNA molecule, called a double helix, looks like a twisted ladder. The sides of the ladder are made of smaller sugar-phosphate molecules.

DNA

Proteins

C The rungs of the ladder are paired nitrogen bases. Notice that the pairs fit together much like puzzle pieces.

Guanine   Cytosine   Adenine   Thymine   Phosphate   Sugar (deoxyribose)

DNA's Structure In 1952, scientist Rosalind Franklin discovered that DNA is two chains of molecules in a spiral form. By using an X-ray technique, Dr. Franklin showed that the large spiral was probably made up of two spirals. As it turned out, the structure of DNA is similar to a twisted ladder. In 1953, using the work of Franklin and others, scientists James Watson and Francis Crick made a model of a DNA molecule.

A DNA Model What does DNA look like? According to the Watson and Crick DNA model, each side of the ladder is made up of sugar-phosphate molecules. Each molecule consists of the sugar called deoxyribose (dee AHK sih ri bohs) and a phosphate group. The rungs of the ladder are made up of other molecules called nitrogen bases. Four kinds of nitrogen bases are found in DNA—adenine (AD un een), guanine (GWAHN een), cytosine (SITE uh seen), and thymine (THI meen). The bases are represented by the letters A, G, C, and T. The amount of cytosine in cells always equals the amount of guanine, and the amount of adenine always equals the amount of thymine. This led to the hypothesis that these bases occur as pairs in DNA. **Figure 14** shows that adenine always pairs with thymine, and guanine always pairs with cytosine. Like interlocking pieces of a puzzle, each base bonds only with its correct partner.

✓ **Reading Check** *What are the nitrogen base pairs in a DNA molecule?*

TRY AT HOME
Mini LAB

Modeling DNA Replication

Procedure
1. Suppose you have a segment of DNA that is six nitrogen base pairs in length. On **paper,** using the letters A, T, C, and G, write a combination of six pairs remembering that A and T are always a pair and C and G are always a pair.
2. Duplicate your segment of DNA. On paper, diagram how this happens and show the new DNA segments.

Analysis
Compare the order of bases of the original DNA to the new DNA molecules.

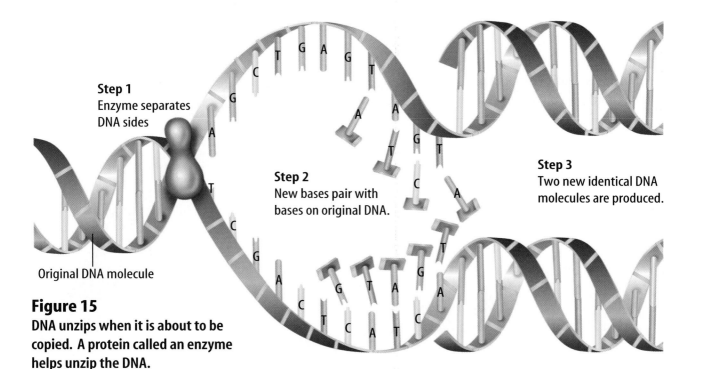

Step 1
Enzyme separates DNA sides

Step 2
New bases pair with bases on original DNA.

Step 3
Two new identical DNA molecules are produced.

Original DNA molecule

Figure 15
DNA unzips when it is about to be copied. A protein called an enzyme helps unzip the DNA.

Figure 16
This diagram shows just a few of the genes that have been identified on human chromosome 7. The bold print is the name that has been given to each gene.

Chromosome 7

GCK
Diabetes

ELN
Williams syndrome
Physical- and mental-development disorder

Pendrin
Pendred syndrome
A form of deafness

CFTR
Cystic fibrosis

OB
Obesity

Copying DNA When chromosomes are duplicated before mitosis or meiosis, the amount of DNA in the nucleus is doubled. The Watson and Crick model shows how this takes place. The two sides of DNA unwind and separate. Each side then becomes a pattern on which a new side forms, as shown in **Figure 15.** The new DNA has bases that are identical to those of the original DNA and are in the same order.

Genes

Most of your characteristics, such as the color of your hair, your height, and even how things taste to you, depend on the kinds of proteins your cells make. DNA in your cells stores the instructions for making these proteins.

Proteins build cells and tissues or work as enzymes. The instructions for making a specific protein are found in a **gene** which is a section of DNA on a chromosome. Each chromosome may contain hundreds of genes, as shown in **Figure 16.** Proteins are made of chains of hundreds or thousands of amino acids. The gene determines the order of amino acids in a protein. Changing the order of the amino acids makes a different protein. What might occur if an important protein couldn't be made or if the wrong protein was made in your cells?

Making Proteins Genes are found in the nucleus, but proteins are made on ribosomes in cytoplasm. The codes for making proteins are carried from the nucleus to the ribosomes by another type of nucleic acid called ribonucleic acid, or **RNA.**

Ribonucleic Acid RNA is made in the nucleus on a DNA pattern. However, RNA is different from DNA. If DNA is like a ladder, RNA is like a ladder that has all its rungs sawed in half. Compare the DNA molecule in **Figure 14** to the RNA molecule in **Figure 17.** RNA has the bases A, G, and C like DNA but has the base uracil (U) instead of thymine (T). The sugar-phosphate molecules in RNA contain the sugar ribose, not deoxyribose.

The three main kinds of RNA made from DNA in a cell's nucleus are messenger RNA (mRNA), ribosomal RNA (rRNA), and transfer RNA (tRNA). Protein production begins when mRNA moves into the cytoplasm. There, ribosomes attach to it. Ribosomes are made of rRNA. Transfer RNA molecules in the cytoplasm bring amino acids to these ribosomes. Inside the ribosomes, three nitrogen bases on the mRNA temporarily match with three nitrogen bases on the tRNA. The same thing happens for the mRNA and another tRNA molecule, as shown in **Figure 17.** The amino acids that are attached to the two tRNA molecules bond. This is the beginning of a protein. The code carried on the mRNA directs the order in which the amino acids bond. After a tRNA molecule has lost its amino acid, it can move about the cytoplasm and pick up another amino acid just like the first one. The ribosome moves along the mRNA. New tRNA molecules with amino acids match up and add amino acids to the protein molecule.

SCIENCE *Online*

Data Update The Human Genome Project was begun in 1990. One of its goals is to identify all of the genes on human chromosomes. To find out how the project is progressing, visit the Glencoe Science Web site at **science.glencoe.com.** Communicate to your class what you learn.

Figure 17
Cells need DNA, RNA, and amino acids to make proteins.

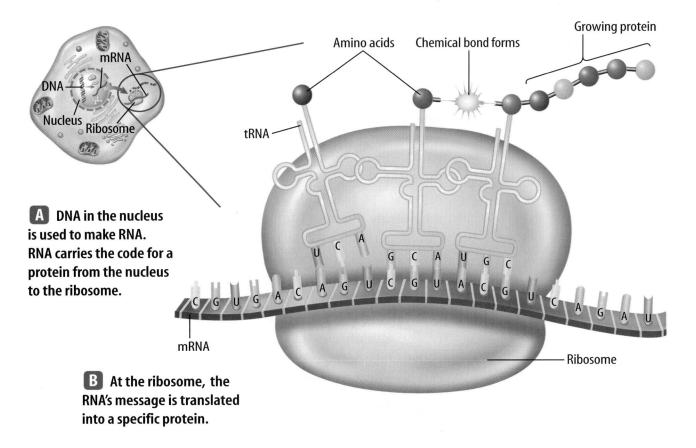

A DNA in the nucleus is used to make RNA. RNA carries the code for a protein from the nucleus to the ribosome.

B At the ribosome, the RNA's message is translated into a specific protein.

Cells in the iris of the eye produce proteins needed for eye color.

Muscle cells produce proteins that result in making muscles move.

Cells in the stomach produce proteins necessary for that cell to digest food.

Figure 18
Each cell in the body produces only the proteins that are necessary to do its job.

Controlling Genes You might think that because most cells in an organism have exactly the same chromosomes and the same genes, they would make the same proteins, but they don't. In many-celled organisms like you, each cell uses only some of the thousands of genes that it has to make proteins. Just as each actor uses only the lines from the script for his or her role, each cell uses only the genes that direct the making of proteins that it needs. For example, muscle proteins are made in muscle cells but not in nerve cells, as shown in **Figure 18.**

Cells must be able to control genes by turning some genes off and turning other genes on. They do this in many different ways. Sometimes the DNA is twisted so tightly that no RNA can be made. Other times, chemicals bind to the DNA so that it cannot be used. If the incorrect proteins are produced, the organism cannot function properly.

Mutations

Sometimes mistakes happen when DNA is being copied. Imagine that the copy of the script the director gave you was missing three pages. You use your copy to learn your lines. When you begin rehearsing for the play, everyone is ready for one of the scenes except for you. What happened? You check your copy of the script against the original and find that three of the pages are missing. Because your script is different from the others, you cannot perform your part correctly.

If DNA is not copied exactly, the proteins made from the instructions may not be made correctly. These mistakes, called **mutations,** are any permanent change in the DNA sequence of a gene or chromosome of a cell. Some mutations include cells that receive an entire extra chromosome or are missing a chromosome. Outside factors such as X rays, sunlight, and some chemicals have been known to cause mutations.

Reading Check *When are mutations likely to occur?*

Figure 19
Because of a defect on chromosome 2, the mutant fruit fly has short wings and cannot fly. *Could this defect be transferred to the mutant's offspring? Explain.*

Results of a Mutation Genes control the traits you inherit. Without correctly coded proteins, an organism can't grow, repair, or maintain itself. A change in a gene or chromosome can change the traits of an organism, as illustrated in **Figure 19.**

If the mutation occurs in a body cell, it might or might not be life threatening to the organism. However, if a mutation occurs in a sex cell, then all the cells that are formed from that sex cell will have that mutation. Mutations add variety to a species when the organism reproduces. Many mutations are harmful to organisms, often causing their death. Some mutations do not appear to have any effect on the organism, and some can even be beneficial. For example, a mutation to a plant might cause it to produce a chemical that certain insects avoid. If these insects normally eat the plant, the mutation will help the plant survive.

SCIENCE *Online*

Research Visit the Glencoe Science Web site at **science.glencoe.com** for more information about what genes are present on the chromosomes of a fruit fly. Make a poster that shows one of the chromosomes and some of the genes found on that chromosome.

Section 3 Assessment

1. How does DNA make a copy of itself?
2. How are the codes for proteins carried from the nucleus to the ribosomes?
3. A single strand of DNA has the bases AGTAAC. Using letters, show a matching DNA strand from this pattern.
4. How is tRNA used when cells build proteins?
5. **Think Critically** You begin as one cell. Compare the DNA in one of your brain cells to the DNA in one of your heart cells.

Skill Builder Activities

6. **Concept Mapping** Using a network tree concept map, show how DNA and RNA are alike and how they are different. **For more help, refer to the** Science Skill Handbook.

7. **Using a Word Processor** Use a word processor to make an outline of the events that led up to the discovery of DNA. Use library resources to find this information. **For more help, refer to the** Technology Skill Handbook.

Activity
Use the Internet

Mutations

Mutations can result in dominant genes or recessive genes. Two recessive genes are needed to make a trait appear. You need only one gene of a dominant gene for a trait to appear. Why do some mutations become common traits while others don't?

Recognize the Problem

How can a mutation become a common trait?

Form a Hypothesis

Form a hypothesis about how a mutation can become a common trait.

Fantail Pigeon

Goals
- **Observe** traits of various animals.
- **Research** how mutations become traits.
- Gather data about mutations.
- Make a frequency table of your findings and communicate them to other students.

Data Source
SCIENCE_Online_ Go to the Glencoe Science Web site at **science. glencoe.com** for more information on common genetic traits in different animals, recessive and dominant genes, and data from other students.

White tiger

Test Your Hypothesis

Plan

1. **Observe** common traits in various animals, such as household pets or animals you might see in a zoo.

2. **Learn** what genes carry these traits in each animal.

3. **Research** the traits to discover which ones are results of mutations. Are all mutations dominant? Are any of these mutations beneficial?

Do

1. Make sure your teacher approves your plan before you start.

2. Visit the Glencoe Science Web site for links to different sites about mutations and genetics.

3. **Research** various traits to discover whether or not they are mutations.

4. **Decide** if a mutation is beneficial, harmful, or neither. Record your data in your Science Journal.

Siberian Husky's eyes

Analyze Your Data

1. **Record** in your Science Journal a list of traits that are results of mutations.

2. **Describe** an animal, such as a pet or an animal you've seen in the zoo. Point out which traits are known to be the result of a mutation.

3. Make a chart that compares recessive mutations to dominant mutations. Which are more common?

4. Share your data with other students by posting it on the Glencoe Science Web site.

Draw Conclusions

1. **Compare** your findings to those of your classmates and other data on the Glencoe Science Web site. What were some of the traits your classmates found that you did not? Which were the most common?

2. Look at your chart of mutations. Are all mutations beneficial? When might a mutation be harmful to an organism?

3. How would your data be affected if you had performed this activity when one of these common mutations first appeared? Do you think you would see more or less animals with this trait?

4. Mutations occur every day but we only see a few of them. Infer how many mutations over millions of years can lead to a new species.

Communicating Your Data

SCIENCE Online Find this *Use the Internet* activity on the Glencoe Science Web site at **science.glencoe.com.** **Post** your data in the table provided. Combine your data with that of other students and make a chart that shows all of the data.

Oops! Accidents in SCIENCE

SOMETIMES GREAT DISCOVERIES HAPPEN BY ACCIDENT!

A Tangled

How did a scientist get chromosomes to separate?

Thanks to chromosomes, each of us is unique!

Viewed under a microscope, chromosomes in cells sometimes look a lot like tangled spaghetti. That's why during the early 1900s, scientists had such a hard time figuring out how many chromosomes are in each human cell.

Tale

Imagine then, how Dr. Tao-Chiuh Hsu (dow shew•SEW) must have felt when he looked into a microscope and saw "beautifully scattered chromosomes." The problem was, Hsu didn't know what he had done to separate the chromosomes into countable strands.

"I tried to study those slides and set up some more cultures to repeat the miracle," Hsu explained. "But nothing happened."

For three months, Hsu toiled in the lab, changing every variable he could think of to make the chromosomes separate again.

In April 1952, he reduced the amount of salt and increased the amount of water in the solution used to prepare the cells for study, and his efforts were finally rewarded. Hsu quickly realized that the chromosomes separated because of osmosis.

Osmosis is the movement of water molecules through cell membranes. This movement occurs in predictable ways. The water molecules move from areas with higher concentrations of water to areas with lower concentrations of water. In Hsu's case, the solution had a higher concentration of water than the cell did. So water moved from the solution into the cell and the cell swelled until it finally exploded. The chromosomes suddenly were visible as separate strands.

What made the cells swell the first time? Apparently, a lab technician had mixed the solution incorrectly. "Since nearly four months had elapsed, there was no way to trace who actually had prepared that particular [solution]," Hsu noted. "Therefore, this heroine must remain anonymous."

The Real Count

Although Hsu's view of the chromosomes was fairly clear, he mistakenly estimated the number of chromosomes in a human cell. He put the count at 48, which was the number that most scientists of the day accepted. By 1956, however, other scientists improved upon Hsu's techniques and concluded that there are 46 chromosomes in a human cell. Because chromosomes contain the genes that determine each person's characteristics, this discovery helped scientists better understand genetic diseases and disorders. Scientists also have a better idea of why every person, including you, is unique.

These chromosomes are magnified 500 times.

CONNECTIONS Research Until the 1950s, scientists believed that there were 48 chromosomes in a human cell. Research the developments that led scientists to the conclusion that the human cell has 46 chromosomes. Use the Glencoe Science Web site to get started.

SCIENCE *Online*
For more information, visit
science.glencoe.com

Chapter **4** Study Guide

Section 1 Cell Division and Mitosis

1. The life cycle of a cell has two parts—growth and development and cell division. Cell division includes mitosis and the division of the cytoplasm.

2. In mitosis, the nucleus divides to form two identical nuclei. Mitosis occurs in four continuous steps, or phases—prophase, metaphase, anaphase, and telophase.

3. Cell division in animal cells and plant cells is similar, but plant cells do not have centrioles and animal cells do not form cell walls.

4. Organisms use cell division to grow, to replace cells, and for asexual reproduction. Asexual reproduction produces organisms with DNA identical to the parent's DNA. Fission, budding, and regeneration can be used for asexual reproduction. *How would cell division help heal this broken bone?*

Section 2 Sexual Reproduction and Meiosis

1. Sexual reproduction results when a male sex cell enters the female sex cell. This event is called fertilization, and the cell that forms is called the zygote.

2. Before fertilization, meiosis occurs in the reproductive organs, producing four haploid sex cells from one diploid cell.

3. During meiosis, two divisions of the nucleus occur.

4. Meiosis ensures that offspring produced by fertilization have the same number of chromosomes as their parents. *If the diploid number of a frog is 26, how many chromosomes does this tadpole have?*

Section 3 DNA

1. DNA—the genetic material of all organisms—is a large molecule made up of two twisted strands of sugar-phosphate molecules and nitrogen bases.

2. All cells contain DNA. The section of DNA on a chromosome that directs the making of a specific protein is a gene.

3. DNA can copy itself and is the pattern from which RNA is made. Messenger RNA, ribosomal RNA, and transfer RNA are used to make proteins.

4. Sometimes changes in DNA occur. Permanent changes in DNA are called mutations. *Why does this fruit fly have four wings instead of the normal two?*

After You Read

FOLDABLES Reading & Study Skills

To help you review cell reproduction, use the Organizational Study Fold about the cell you made at the beginning of the chapter.

Visualizing Main Ideas

Think of four ways that organisms can use mitosis and fill out the spider diagram below.

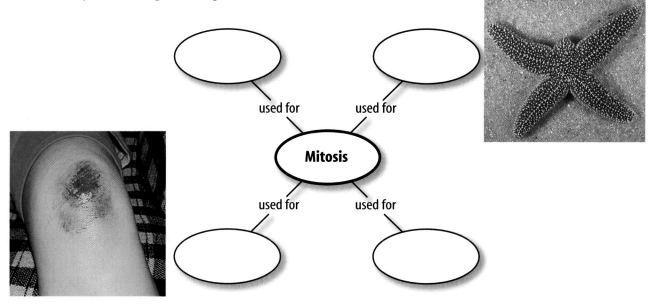

used for

used for

Mitosis

used for

used for

Vocabulary Review

Vocabulary Words

a. asexual reproduction
b. chromosome
c. diploid
d. DNA
e. egg
f. fertilization
g. gene
h. haploid
i. meiosis
j. mitosis
k. mutation
l. RNA
m. sexual reproduction
n. sperm
o. zygote

THE PRINCETON REVIEW **Study Tip**

Be a teacher—organize a group of friends and instruct each person to review a section of the chapter for the group. Teaching helps you remember and understand information thoroughly.

Using Vocabulary

Replace each underlined word in the following statements with the correct vocabulary word.

1. <u>Muscle</u> and <u>skin</u> cells are sex cells.

2. <u>Digestion</u> produces two identical cells.

3. An example of a nucleic acid is <u>sugar</u>.

4. A <u>cell</u> is the code for a protein.

5. A <u>diploid</u> sperm is formed during meiosis.

6. Budding is a type of <u>meiosis</u>.

7. A <u>ribosome</u> is a structure in the nucleus that contains hereditary material.

8. <u>Respiration</u> produces four sex cells.

9. As a result of <u>fission</u>, a new organism develops that has its own unique identity.

10. An error made during the copying of DNA is called a <u>protein</u>.

Chapter 4 Assessment

Checking Concepts

Choose the word or phrase that best answers the question.

1. Which of the following is a double spiral molecule with pairs of nitrogen bases?
   - **A)** RNA
   - **B)** amino acid
   - **C)** protein
   - **D)** DNA

2. What is in RNA but NOT in DNA?
   - **A)** thymine
   - **B)** thyroid
   - **C)** adenine
   - **D)** uracil

3. If a diploid tomato cell has 24 chromosomes, how many chromosomes will the tomato's sex cells have?
   - **A)** 6
   - **B)** 12
   - **C)** 24
   - **D)** 48

4. During a cell's life cycle, when do chromosomes duplicate?
   - **A)** anaphase
   - **B)** metaphase
   - **C)** interphase
   - **D)** telophase

5. When do chromatids separate during mitosis?
   - **A)** anaphase
   - **B)** prophase
   - **C)** metaphase
   - **D)** telophase

6. How many chromosomes are in the original cell compared to those in the new cells formed by cell division?
   - **A)** the same amount
   - **B)** half as many
   - **C)** twice as many
   - **D)** four times as many

7. What can budding, fission, and regeneration be used for?
   - **A)** mutations
   - **B)** sexual reproduction
   - **C)** cell cycles
   - **D)** asexual reproduction

8. What is any permanent change in a gene or a chromosome called?
   - **A)** fission
   - **B)** reproduction
   - **C)** replication
   - **D)** mutation

9. What does meiosis produce?
   - **A)** cells with the diploid chromosome number
   - **B)** cells with identical chromosomes
   - **C)** sex cells
   - **D)** a zygote

10. What type of nucleic acid carries the codes for making proteins from the nucleus to the ribosome?
    - **A)** DNA
    - **B)** RNA
    - **C)** protein
    - **D)** genes

Thinking Critically

11. If the sequence of bases on one side of DNA is ATCCGTC, what is the sequence on its other side?

12. A strand of RNA made using the DNA pattern ATCCGTC would have what base sequence? Look at **Figure 14** for a hint.

13. Will a mutation in a human skin cell be passed on to the person's offspring? Explain.

14. What occurs in mitosis that gives the new cells identical DNA?

15. How could a zygote end up with an extra chromosome?

Developing Skills

16. **Classifying** Copy and complete this table about DNA and RNA.

DNA and RNA		
	DNA	**RNA**
Number of Strands		
Type of Sugar		
Letter Names of Bases		
Where Found		

17. Concept Mapping Complete the events chain concept map of DNA synthesis.

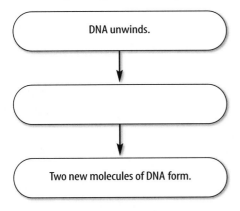

DNA unwinds.

↓

↓

Two new molecules of DNA form.

18. Comparing and Contrasting Make a table about mitosis and meiosis. Include the number of divisions, number of cells produced, and chromosomes in parent cells and in sex cells.

19. Forming Hypotheses Make a hypothesis about the effect of an incorrect mitotic division on the new cells produced.

20. Concept Mapping Make an events chain concept map of what occurs from interphase in the parent cell to the formation of the zygote. Tell whether the chromosome's number at each stage is haploid or diploid.

Performance Assessment

21. Flash Cards Make a set of 11 flash cards with drawings of a cell that show the different stages of meiosis. Shuffle your cards and then put them in the correct order. Give them to another student in the class to try.

TECHNOLOGY

Go to the Glencoe Science Web site at **science.glencoe.com** or use the **Glencoe Science CD-ROM** for additional chapter assessment.

THE PRINCETON REVIEW **Test Practice**

A scientist studied the reproduction of human skin cells. The scientist examined several skin cells using a microscope. The table below summarizes what she learned.

Skin Cells		
Cell	Phase of Division	Characteristic
1	Anaphase	Chromosome separation
2	Telophase	Cytoplasm division
3	Prophase	Visible chromosomes
4	Metaphase	Chromosomes line up

Use the information in the table to answer the following questions.

1. What process is taking place in all of the cells?
A) cell division
B) fertilization
C) cytoplasm division
D) chromosome separation

2. Which is the correct order of the stages, from first to last, in the cell division of a skin cell?
F) 3, 4, 1, 2   **H)** 1, 2, 4, 3
G) 1, 3, 2, 4   **J)** 2, 1, 3, 4

3. Since the process described in the table produces two new identical cells, before it begins the chromosomes in the cell must _____ .
A) divide in half   **C)** duplicate
B) find a mate   **D)** disintegrate

5

Heredity

Wherever you go, look around you. You don't have the same skin color, the same kind of hair, or the same height as everyone else. Why do you resemble some people but do not look like others at all? In this chapter, you'll find out how differences are determined, and you will learn how to predict when certain traits might appear. You also will learn what causes some hereditary disorders.

What do you think?

Science Journal Look at the picture below with a classmate. Discuss what you think this might be or what is happening. Here's a hint: *The secret to why you look the way you do is found in this picture.* Write your answer or best guess in your Science Journal.

EXPLORE ACTIVITY

You and your best friend enjoy the same sports, like the same food, and even have similar haircuts. But, there are noticeable differences between your appearances. Most of these differences are controlled by the genes you inherited from your parents. In the following activity, you will observe one of these differences.

Observe dimples on faces

1. Notice the two students in the photographs. One student has dimples when she smiles, and the other student doesn't have dimples.

2. Ask your classmates to smile naturally. In your Science Journal, record the name of each classmate and whether each one has dimples.

Observe

In your Science Journal, calculate the percentage of students who have dimples. Are facial dimples a common feature among your classmates?

Before You Read

FOLDABLES
Reading & Study Skills

Making a Classify Study Fold As you read this chapter about heredity, you can use the following Foldable to help you classify characteristics. When you classify, you organize objects or events into groups based on their common features.

Personal Characteristics	Inherited	Not Inherited
eyes		
hair		
dimples		

1. Place a sheet of paper in front of you so the short side is at the top. Fold both sides in to divide the paper into thirds. Unfold the paper so three columns show.

2. Fold the paper in half from top to bottom. Then fold it in half again two more times. Unfold all the folds.

3. Trace over all the fold lines and label the columns you created: *Personal Characteristics*, *Inherited*, and *Not Inherited*, as shown. List personal characteristics down the left-hand column, as shown.

4. Before you read the chapter, predict which characteristics are inherited or not inherited. As you read the chapter, check and change the table.

① Genetics

What You'll Learn

- **Explain** how traits are inherited.
- **Identify** Mendel's role in the history of genetics.
- **Use** a Punnett square to predict the results of crosses.
- **Compare and contrast** the difference between an individual's genotype and phenotype.

Vocabulary

heredity	Punnett square
allele	genotype
genetics	phenotype
hybrid	homozygous
dominant	heterozygous
recessive	

Why It's Important

Heredity and genetics help explain why people are different.

Inheriting Traits

Do you look more like one parent or grandparent? Do you have your father's eyes? What about Aunt Isabella's cheekbones? Eye color, nose shape, and many other physical features are some of the traits that are inherited from parents, as **Figure 1** shows. An organism is a collection of traits, all inherited from its parents. **Heredity** (huh REH duh tee) is the passing of traits from parent to offspring. What controls these traits?

What is genetics? Generally, genes on chromosomes control an organism's form and function. The different forms of a trait that a gene may have are called **alleles** (uh LEELZ). When a pair of chromosomes separates during meiosis (mi OH sus), alleles for each trait also separate into different sex cells. As a result, every sex cell has one allele for each trait, as shown in **Figure 2.** The allele in one sex cell may control one form of the trait, such as having facial dimples. The allele in the other sex cell may control a different form of the trait—not having dimples. The study of how traits are inherited through the interactions of alleles is the science of **genetics** (juh NET ihks).

Figure 1
Note the strong family resemblance among these four generations.

Figure 2

An allele is one form of a gene. Alleles separate into separate sex cells during meiosis. In this example, the alleles that control the trait for dimples include *D,* the presence of dimples, and *d,* the absence of dimples.

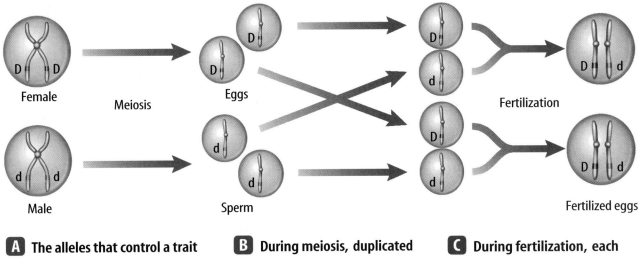

Female Meiosis Eggs Fertilization

Male Sperm Fertilized eggs

A The alleles that control a trait are located on each duplicated chromosome.

B During meiosis, duplicated chromosomes separate.

C During fertilization, each parent donates one chromosome. This results in two alleles for the trait of dimples in the new individual formed.

Mendel—The Father of Genetics

Did you know that an experiment with pea plants helped scientists understand why your eyes are the color that they are? Gregor Mendel was an Austrian monk who studied mathematics and science but became a gardener in a monastery. His interest in plants began as a boy in his father's orchard where he could predict the possible types of flowers and fruits that would result from crossbreeding two plants. Curiosity about the connection between the color of a pea flower and the type of seed that same plant produced inspired him to begin experimenting with garden peas in 1856. Mendel made careful use of scientific methods, which resulted in the first recorded study of how traits pass from one generation to the next. After eight years, Mendel presented his results with pea plants to scientists.

Before Mendel, scientists mostly relied on observation and description, and often studied many traits at one time. Mendel was the first to trace one trait through several generations. He was also the first to use the mathematics of probability to explain heredity. The use of math in plant science was a new concept and not widely accepted then. Mendel's work was forgotten for a long time. In 1900, three plant scientists, working separately, reached the same conclusions as Mendel. Each plant scientist had discovered Mendel's writings while doing his own research. Since then, Mendel has been known as the father of genetics.

Research Visit the Glencoe Science Web site at **science.glencoe.com** for more information about early genetics experiments. Write a paragraph in your Science Journal about a scientist, other than Gregor Mendel, who studied genetics.

Table 1 Traits Compared by Mendel							
Traits	Shape of Seeds	Color of Seeds	Color of Pods	Shape of Pods	Plant Height	Position of Flowers	Flower Color
Dominant Trait	Round	Yellow	Green	Full	Tall	At leaf junctions	Purple
Recessive Trait	Wrinkled	Green	Yellow	Flat, constricted	Short	At tips of branches	White

TRY AT HOME

Mini LAB

Comparing Common Traits

Procedure

1. Safely survey as many **dogs** in your neighborhood as you can for the presence of a solid color or spotted coat, short or long hair, and floppy ears or ears that stand up straight.
2. Make a data table that lists each of the traits. Record your data in the data table.

Analysis

1. Compare the number of dogs that have one form of a trait with those that have the other form. How do those two groups compare?
2. What can you conclude about the variations you noticed in the dogs?

Genetics in a Garden

Each time Mendel crossed two plants with different expressions of a trait to study that trait, he found that the new plants all looked like one of the two parents. He called these new plants **hybrids** (HI brudz) because they receive different genetic information, or different alleles, for a trait from each parent. These results made Mendel even more curious about how traits are inherited.

Garden peas are easy to breed for pure traits. An organism that always produces the same traits generation after generation is called a purebred. For example, tall plants that always produce seeds that produce tall plants are purebred for the trait of tall height. **Table 1** shows other pea plant traits Mendel studied.

Reading Check *Why might farmers plant purebred crop seeds?*

Dominant and Recessive Factors In nature, insects randomly pollinate plants as they move from flower to flower. In his experiments, Mendel used pollen from the flowers of purebred tall plants to pollinate by hand the flowers of purebred short plants. This process is called cross-pollination. He found that tall plants crossed with short plants produced seeds that produced all tall plants. Whatever caused the plants to be short had disappeared. Mendel called the tall form the **dominant** (DAHM uh nunt) factor because it dominated, or covered up, the short form. He called the form that seemed to disappear the **recessive** (rih SES ihv) factor. Today, these are called dominant alleles and recessive alleles. What happened to the recessive form? **Figure 3** answers this question.

Figure 3

Gregor Mendel discovered that the experiments he carried out on garden plants provided an understanding of heredity. For eight years he crossed plants that had different characteristics and recorded how those characteristics were passed from generation to generation. One such characteristic, or trait, was the color of pea pods. The results of Mendel's experiment on pea pod color are shown below.

Parents

1st Generation

A One of the so-called "parent plants" in Mendel's experiment had pods that were green, a dominant trait. The other parent plant had pods that were yellow, a recessive trait.

B Mendel discovered that the two "parents" produced a generation of plants with green pods. The recessive color—yellow—did not appear in any of the pods.

2nd Generation

C Next, Mendel collected seeds from the first-generation plants and raised a second generation. He discovered that these second-generation plants produced plants with either green or yellow pods in a ratio of about three plants with green pods for every one plant with yellow pods. The recessive trait had reappeared. This 3:1 ratio proved remarkably consistent in hundreds of similar crosses, allowing Mendel to accurately predict the ratio of pod color in second-generation plants.

Using Probability to Make Predictions If you and your sister can't agree on what movie to see, you could solve the problem by tossing a coin. When you toss a coin, you're dealing with probabilities. Probability is a branch of mathematics that helps you predict the chance that something will happen. If your sister chooses tails while the coin is in the air, what is the probability that the coin will land tail-side up? Because a coin has two sides, there are two possible outcomes, heads or tails. One outcome is tails. Therefore, the probability of one side of a coin showing is one out of two, or 50 percent.

Mendel also dealt with probabilities. One of the things that made his predictions accurate was that he worked with large numbers of plants. He studied almost 30,000 pea plants over a period of eight years. By doing so, Mendel increased his chances of seeing a repeatable pattern. Valid scientific conclusions need to be based on results that can be duplicated.

Punnett Squares Suppose you wanted to know what colors of pea plant flowers you would get if you pollinated white flowers on one pea plant with pollen from purple flowers on a different plant. How could you predict what the offspring would look like without making the cross? A handy tool used to predict results in Mendelian genetics is the **Punnett** (PUN ut) **square.** In a Punnett square, letters represent dominant and recessive alleles. An uppercase letter stands for a dominant allele. A lowercase letter stands for a recessive allele. The letters are a form of code. They show the **genotype** (JEE nuh tipe), or genetic makeup, of an organism. Once you understand what the letters mean, you can tell a lot about the inheritance of a trait in an organism.

The way an organism looks and behaves as a result of its genotype is its **phenotype** (FEE nuh tipe), as shown in **Figure 4.** If you have brown hair, then the phenotype for your hair color is brown.

Alleles Determine Traits Most cells in your body have two alleles for every trait. These alleles are located on chromosomes within the nucleus of cells. An organism with two alleles that are the same is called **homozygous** (hoh muh ZI gus). For Mendel's peas, this would be written as *TT* (homozygous for the tall-dominant trait) or *tt* (homozygous for the short-recessive trait). An organism that has two different alleles for a trait is called **heterozygous** (het uh roh ZI gus). The hybrid plants Mendel produced were all heterozygous for height, *Tt.*

Figure 4
This snapdragon's phenotype is red. *Can you tell what the flower's genotype for color is? Explain your answer.*

✔ **Reading Check** *What is the difference between homozygous and heterozygous organisms?*

Making a Punnett Square In a Punnett square for predicting one trait, the letters representing the two alleles from one parent are written along the top of the grid, one letter per section. Those of the second parent are placed down the side of the grid, one letter per section. Each square of the grid is filled in with one allele donated by each parent. The letters that you use to fill in each of the squares represent the genotypes of possible offspring that the parents could produce.

Math Skills Activity

Calculating Probability Using a Punnett Square

You can determine the probability of certain traits by using a Punnett square. Letters are used to represent the two alleles from each parent and are combined to determine the possible genotypes of the offspring.

Example Problem
One dog carries heterozygous, black-fur traits (Bb), and its mate carries homogeneous, blond-fur traits (bb). Calculate the probability of the puppy having black fur.

Solution

1 *This is what you know:*
dominant allele is represented by *B*
recessive allele is represented by *b*

2 *This is what you need to find:*
the probability of a puppy's fur color being black using a Punnett square

3 *This is the diagram you need to use:*

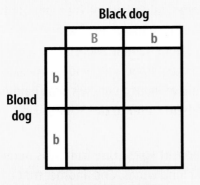

4 *Complete the Punnett square by taking each letter in each column and combining it with each letter from each row in the corresponding square.*

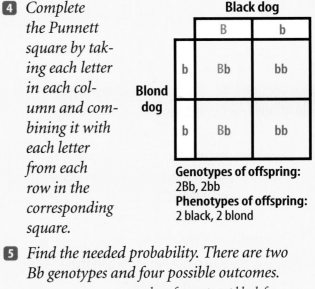

Genotypes of offspring:
2Bb, 2bb
Phenotypes of offspring:
2 black, 2 blond

5 *Find the needed probability. There are two Bb genotypes and four possible outcomes.*

$$P(black\ fur) = \frac{number\ of\ ways\ to\ get\ black\ fur}{number\ of\ possible\ outcomes}$$

$$= \frac{2}{4} = \frac{1}{2} = 50\%$$

Practice Problem

Use a Punnett square to determine the probability of each of the offspring's genotype and phenotype when two heterozygous, tall-dominant traits (Tt) are crossed with each other.

For more help, refer to the Math Skill Handbook.

Principles of Heredity Even though Gregor Mendel didn't know anything about DNA, genes, or chromosomes, he succeeded in beginning to describe and mathematically represent how inherited traits are passed from parents to offspring. He realized that some factor in the pea plant produced certain traits. Mendel also concluded that these factors separated when the pea plant reproduced. Mendel arrived at his conclusions after years of detailed observation, careful analysis, and repeated experimentation. **Table 2** summarizes Mendel's principles of heredity.

Table 2 Principles of Heredity	
1 Traits are controlled by alleles on chromosomes.	
2 An allele's effect is dominant or recessive.	
3 When a pair of chromosomes separates during meiosis, the different alleles for a trait move into separate sex cells.	

Section ① Assessment

1. Alleles are described as being dominant or recessive. What is the difference between a dominant and a recessive allele?

2. How are dominant and recessive alleles represented in a Punnett square?

3. Explain the difference between genotype and phenotype. Give examples.

4. Gregor Mendel, an Austrian monk who lived in the 1800s, is known as the father of genetics. Explain why Mendel has been given this title.

5. **Think Critically** If an organism expresses a recessive phenotype, can you tell the genotype? Explain your answer by giving an example.

Skill Builder Activities

6. **Predicting** Hairline shape is an inherited trait in humans. The widow's peak allele is dominant, and the straight hairline allele is recessive. Predict how both parents with widow's peaks could have a child without a widow's peak hairline. **For more help, refer to the** Science Skill Handbook.

7. **Using Percentages** One fruit fly is heterozygous for long wings, and another fruit fly is homozygous for short wings. Long wings are dominant to short wings. Using a Punnett square, find out what percent of the offspring are expected to have short wings. **For more help, refer to the** Math Skill Handbook.

Activity

Predicting Results

Could you predict how many brown rabbits would result from crossing two heterozygous black rabbits? Brown color is a recessive trait for hair color in rabbits. Try this investigation to find out.

What You'll Investigate
How does chance affect combinations of genes?

Materials
paper bags (2)   white beans (100)
red beans (100)

Goals
- **Model** chance events in heredity.
- **Compare and contrast** predicted and actual results.

Safety Precautions
WARNING: *Do not taste, eat, or drink any materials used in the lab.*

Procedure

1. Use a Punnett square to predict how many red/red, red/white, and white/white bean combinations are possible. The combinations represent the coat colors in rabbit offspring.

2. Place 50 red beans and 50 white beans in a paper bag. Place 50 red beans and 50 white beans in a second bag. Red beans represent black alleles and white beans represent brown alleles.

3. Label one of the bags *female* for the female parent. Label the other bag *male* for the male parent.

4. Use a data table to record the combination each time you remove two beans. Your table will need to accommodate 100 picks.

5. Without looking, remove one bean from each bag. The two beans represent the alleles that combine when sperm and egg join. After recording, return the beans to their bags.

6. **Count** and record the total numbers for each of the three combinations in your data table.

7. **Compile** and record the class totals.

Conclude and Apply

1. Which combination occurred most often?

2. **Calculate** the ratio of red/red to red/white to white/white. What hair color in rabbits do these combinations represent?

3. **Compare** your predicted (expected) results with your observed (actual) results.

4. **Hypothesize** how you could get predicted results to be closer to actual results.

Gene Combinations			
Rabbits	**Red/ Red**	**Red/ White**	**White/ White**
Your Total			
Class Total			

Communicating Your Data

Write a paragraph that clearly describes your results. Have another student read your paragraph. Ask if he or she could understand what happened. If not, rewrite your paragraph and have the other student read it again. **For more help, refer to the** Science Skill Handbook.

Genetics Since Mendel

As You Read

What You'll Learn

- **Explain** how traits are inherited by incomplete dominance.
- **Compare** multiple alleles and polygenic inheritance, and give examples of each.
- **Describe** two human genetic disorders and how they are inherited.
- **Explain** how sex-linked traits are passed to offspring.

Vocabulary

incomplete dominance
polygenic inheritance
sex-linked gene

Why It's Important

Most of your inherited traits involve more complex patterns of inheritance than Mendel discovered.

Incomplete Dominance

Not even in science do things remain the same. After Mendel's work was rediscovered in 1900, scientists repeated his experiments, and for some plants, such as peas, Mendel's results proved true. However, when different plants were crossed, the results were sometimes different. One scientist crossed purebred red four-o'clock plants with purebred white four-o'clock plants. He expected to get all red flowers, but they were pink. Neither allele for flower color seemed dominant. Had the colors become blended like paint colors? He crossed the pink-flowered plants with each other, and red, pink, and white flowers were produced. The red and white alleles had not become blended. Instead, when the allele for white flowers and the allele for red flowers combined, the result was an intermediate phenotype—a pink flower. Similar results for horses are shown in **Figure 5. Incomplete dominance** produces a phenotype that is intermediate between the two homozygous parents. Feather color in some types of chickens also is inherited by incomplete dominance.

Figure 5

These Punnett squares show how the color of horses may be inherited by incomplete dominance. **A** When a chestnut horse is bred with **B** a white horse, all the offspring will be Appaloosa, as shown in **C**, the first Punnett square. **D** When two Appaloosa horses from the offspring are bred, many phenotypes are produced as illustrated in **E**, the second Punnett square. *What is the ratio of the different phenotypes produced in this second generation?*

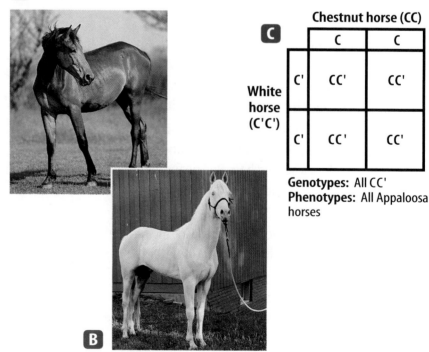

A

B

	Chestnut horse (CC)	
C	C	C
C'	CC'	CC'
C'	CC'	CC'

White horse (C'C')

Genotypes: All CC'
Phenotypes: All Appaloosa horses

Multiple Alleles Mendel studied traits in peas that were controlled by just two alleles. However, many traits are controlled by more than two alleles. A trait that is controlled by more than two alleles is said to be controlled by multiple alleles. Traits controlled by multiple alleles produce more than three phenotypes of that trait.

Imagine that only three types of coins are made—nickels, dimes, and quarters. If every person can have only two coins, six different combinations are possible. In this problem, the coins represent alleles of a trait. The sum of each two-coin combination represents the phenotype. Can you name the six different phenotypes possible with two coins?

Blood type in humans is an example of multiple alleles that produce only four phenotypes. The alleles for blood types are called A, B, and O. The O allele is recessive to both the A and B alleles. When a person inherits one A allele and one B allele for blood type, both are expressed—phenotype AB. A person with phenotype A blood has the genetic makeup, or genotype—AA or AO. Someone with phenotype B blood has the genotype BB or BO. Finally, a person with phenotype O blood has the genotype OO.

 Reading Check *What are the six different blood type genotypes?*

SCIENCE *Online*

Research Visit the Glencoe Science Web site at **science.glencoe.com** for information on the importance of blood types in blood transfusions. In your Science Journal, draw a chart showing which blood types can be used safely during transfusions.

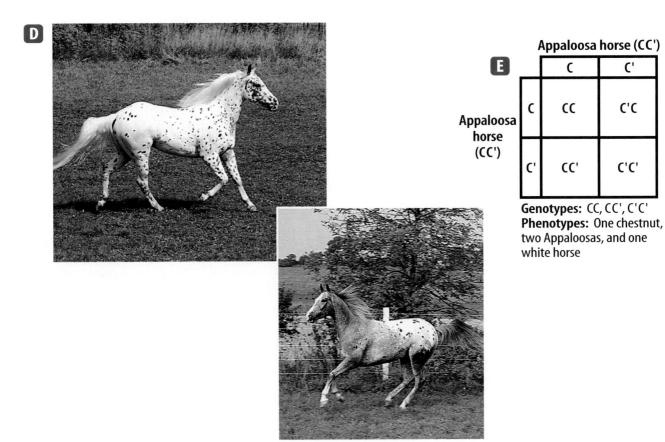

E

	Appaloosa horse (CC')	
	C	**C'**
C	CC	C'C
C'	CC'	C'C'

Appaloosa horse (CC')

Genotypes: CC, CC', C'C'
Phenotypes: One chestnut, two Appaloosas, and one white horse

Procedure

1. Measure the hand spans of your classmates.
2. Using a **ruler,** measure from the tip of the thumb to the tip of the little finger when the hand is stretched out. Read the measurement to the nearest centimeter.
3. Record the name and hand-span measurement of each person in a data table.

Analysis

1. What range of hand spans did you find?
2. Are hand spans inherited as a simple Mendelian pattern or as a polygenic or incomplete dominance pattern? Explain.

Polygenic Inheritance

Eye color is an example of a trait that is produced by a combination of many genes. **Polygenic** (pahl ih JEHN ihk) **inheritance** occurs when a group of gene pairs acts together to produce a trait. The effects of many alleles produces a wide variety of phenotypes. For this reason, it may be hard to classify all the different shades of eye color.

Your height and the color of your eyes and skin are just some of the many human traits controlled by polygenic inheritance. It is estimated that three to six gene pairs control your skin color. Even more gene pairs might control the color of your hair and eyes. The environment also plays an important role in the expression of traits controlled by polygenic inheritance. Polygenic inheritance is common and includes such traits as grain color in wheat and milk production in cows. Egg production in chickens is also a polygenic trait.

Impact of the Environment Your environment plays a role in how some of your genes are expressed or whether they are expressed at all, as shown in **Figure 6.** Environmental influences may be internal or external. For example, most male birds are more brightly colored than females. Chemicals in their bodies determine whether the gene for brightly colored feathers is expressed.

Although genes determine many of your traits, you might be able to influence their expression by the decisions you make. Some people have genes that make them at risk for developing certain cancers. Whether they get cancer might depend on external environmental factors. For instance, if some people at risk for skin cancer limit their exposure to the Sun and take care of their skin, they might never develop cancer.

✓ **Reading Check** *What environmental factors might affect the size of leaves on a tree?*

Figure 6
Himalayan rabbits have alleles for dark-colored fur. However, this allele is able to express itself only at lower temperatures. Only the areas located farthest from the rabbit's main body heat (ears, nose, feet, tail) have dark-colored fur.

Human Genes and Mutations

Sometimes a gene undergoes a change that results in a trait that is expressed differently. Occasionally errors occur in the DNA when it is copied inside of a cell. Such changes and errors are called mutations. Not all mutations are harmful. They might be helpful or have no effect on an organism.

Certain chemicals are known to produce mutations in plants or animals, including humans. X rays and radioactive substances are other causes of some mutations. Mutations are changes in genes.

Chromosome Disorders In addition to individual mutations, problems can occur if the incorrect number of chromosomes is inherited. Every organism has a specific number of chromosomes. However, mistakes in the process of meiosis can result in a new organism with more or fewer chromosomes than normal. A change in the total number of human chromosomes is usually fatal to the unborn embryo or fetus, or the baby may die soon after birth.

Look at the human chromosomes in **Figure 7.** If three copies of chromosome 21 are produced in the fertilized human egg, Down's syndrome results. Individuals with Down's syndrome can be short, exhibit learning disabilities, and have heart problems. Such individuals can lead normal lives if they have no severe health complications.

Figure 7
Humans usually have 23 pairs of chromosomes. Notice that three copies of chromosome 21 are present in this photo, rather than the usual two chromosomes. This change in chromosome number results in Down's syndrome. Chris Burke, a well-known actor, has this syndrome.

Magnification: 10,000×

Figure 8
Sex in many organisms is determined by X and Y chromosomes.
How do the X (left) and Y (right) chromosomes differ from one another in shape and size?

Chemistry
INTEGRATION

People with PKU, a recessive disorder, are missing the enzyme needed to break down a substance found in some artificially sweetened drinks. Soft-drink cans must be labeled to ensure that individuals with this disorder do not unknowingly consume the substance. Explain in your Science Journal how a person can be born with PKU if neither parent has this recessive disorder.

Recessive Genetic Disorders

Most human genetic disorders, such as cystic fibrosis, are caused by recessive genes. Some recessive genes are the result of a mutation within the gene. Many of these alleles are rare. Such genetic disorders occur when both parents have a recessive allele responsible for this disorder. Because the parents are heterozygous, they don't show any symptoms. However, if each parent passes the recessive allele to the child, the child inherits both recessive alleles and will have a recessive genetic disorder.

✔ **Reading Check** *How is cystic fibrosis inherited?*

Cystic fibrosis is a homozygous recessive disorder. It is the most common genetic disorder that may lead to death among Caucasian Americans. In most people, a thin fluid is produced that lubricates the lungs and intestinal tract. People with cystic fibrosis produce thick mucus instead of this thin fluid. The thick mucus builds up in the lungs and makes it hard to breathe. This buildup often results in repeated bacterial respiratory infections. The thick mucus also reduces or prevents the flow of substances necessary for digesting food. Physical therapy, special diets, and new drug therapies have increased the life spans of patients with cystic fibrosis.

Sex Determination

What determines the sex of an individual? Much information on sex inheritance came from studies of fruit flies. Fruit flies have only four pairs of chromosomes. Because the chromosomes are large and few in number, they are easy to study. Scientists identified one pair that contains genes that determine the sex of the organism. They labeled the pair XX in females and XY in males. Geneticists use these labels when studying organisms, including humans. You can see human X and Y chromosomes in **Figure 8.**

Each egg produced by a female normally contains one X chromosome. Males produce sperm that normally have either an X or a Y chromosome. When a sperm with an X chromosome fertilizes an egg, the offspring is a female, XX. A male offspring, XY, is the result of a Y-containing sperm fertilizing an egg. What pair of sex chromosomes is in each of your cells? Sometimes chromosomes do not separate during meiosis. When this occurs, an individual may inherit an abnormal number of sex chromosomes.

Sex-Linked Disorders

Some inherited conditions are linked with the X and Y chromosomes. An allele inherited on a sex chromosome is called a **sex-linked gene.** Color blindness is a sex-linked disorder in which people cannot distinguish between certain colors, particularly red and green. This trait is a recessive allele on the X chromosome. Because males have only one X chromosome, a male with this allele on his X chromosome is color-blind. However, a color-blind female occurs only when both of her X chromosomes have the allele for this trait.

The allele for the distinct patches of three different colors found in calico cats is recessive and carried on the X chromosome. As shown in **Figure 9,** calico cats have inherited two X chromosomes with this recessive allele—one from both parents.

Pedigrees Trace Traits

How can you trace a trait through a family? A pedigree is a visual tool for following a trait through generations of a family. Males are represented by squares and females by circles. A completely filled circle or square shows that the trait is seen in that person. Half-colored circles or squares indicate carriers. A carrier is heterozygous for the trait and it is not seen. People represented by empty circles or squares do not have the trait and are not carriers. The pedigree in **Figure 10** shows how the trait for color blindness is carried through a family.

Female carrier of calico gene (X^CX)

	X^C	X
X^C	X^CX^C	XX^C
Y	X^CY	XY

Male carrier of calico gene (X^CY)

Genotypes: X^CX^C, X^CX, X^CY, XY
Phenotypes: One calico female, one carrier female, one carrier male, one normal male

Figure 9
Calico cat fur is a homozygous recessive sex-linked trait. Female cats that are heterozygous are not calico but are only carriers. Two recessive alleles must be present for this allele to be expressed. *Why aren't all the females calico?*

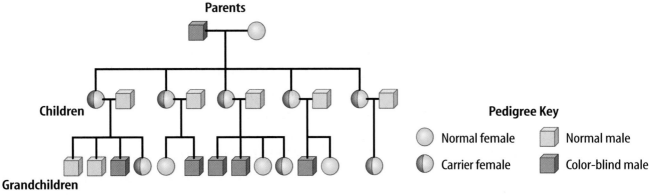

Parents

Children

Grandchildren

Pedigree Key

○ Normal female   ▢ Normal male
◐ Carrier female   ▦ Color-blind male

Figure 10
The symbols in this pedigree's key mean the same thing on all pedigree charts. The grandfather in this family was color-blind and married to a woman who was not a carrier of the color-blind allele. *Why are no women in this family color-blind?*

Figure 11
A variety of traits are considered when breeding dogs. **A** Black Labrador retrievers often are bred to be sporting dogs. **B** Shih tzus are usually companion or show dogs.

What traits are cats bred for? to find out more about cat breeds, see the **Feline Traits Field Guide** at the back of the book.

Using Pedigrees A pedigree is a useful tool for a geneticist. Sometimes a geneticist needs to understand who has had a trait in a family over several generations to determine its pattern of inheritance. A geneticist determines if a trait is recessive, dominant, sex-linked, or has some other pattern of inheritance. When geneticists understand how a trait is inherited, they can predict the probability that a baby will be born with a specific trait.

✔ Reading Check *Why is a pedigree a useful tool for a geneticist?*

Pedigrees also are important in breeding animals or plants. Because livestock and plant crops are used as sources of food, these organisms are bred to increase their yield and nutritional content. Breeders of pets, like the dogs pictured in **Figure 11,** and show animals also examine pedigrees carefully for possible desirable physical and ability traits. Issues concerning health also are considered when researching pedigrees.

Section ② Assessment

1. Compare inheritance by multiple alleles and polygenic inheritance.

2. Explain why a trait inherited by incomplete dominance, such as the color of Appaloosa horses, is not a blend of two alleles.

3. Describe two genetic disorders and discuss how they are inherited.

4. Using a Punnett square, explain why males are affected more often than females by sex-linked genetic disorders.

5. **Think Critically** Calico male cats are rare. Explain how such a cat can exist.

Skill Builder Activities

6. **Predicting** A man with blood type B marries a woman with blood type A. Their first child has blood type O. Predict what other blood types are possible for their future children. Explain your answer using a Punnett square. **For more help, refer to the** Science Skill Handbook.

7. **Communicating** In your Science Journal, write an essay that explains why the offspring of two parents may or may not show much resemblance to either parent. **For more help, refer to the** Science Skill Handbook.

Advances in Genetics

Why is genetics important?

If Mendel were to pick up a daily newspaper in any country today, he'd probably be surprised. News articles about developments in genetic research appear almost daily. The term *gene* has become a common word. The laws of heredity are being used to change the world.

Genetic Engineering

You may know that chromosomes are made of DNA and are in the nucleus of a cell. Sections of DNA in chromosomes that direct cell activities are called genes. Through **genetic engineering,** scientists are experimenting with biological and chemical methods to change the arrangement of DNA that makes up a gene. Genetic engineering already is used to help produce large volumes of medicine. Genes also can be inserted into cells to change how those cells perform their normal functions, as shown in **Figure 12.** Other research is being done to find new ways to improve crop production and quality, including the development of plants that are resistant to disease.

As You Read

What **You'll Learn**
- **Evaluate** the importance of advances in genetics.
- **Sequence** the steps in making genetically engineered organisms.

Vocabulary
genetic engineering

Why **It's Important**
Advances in genetics can affect your health, the foods that you eat, and your environment.

Figure 12
DNA from one organism is placed into another species. This method is used to produce human insulin, human growth hormone, and other chemicals by bacteria.

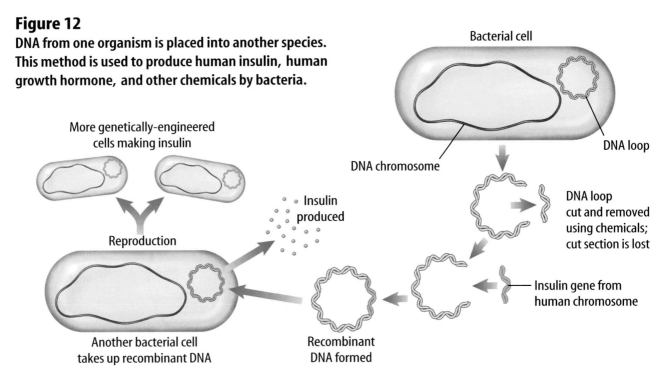

Bacterial cell

DNA chromosome

DNA loop

DNA loop cut and removed using chemicals; cut section is lost

Insulin gene from human chromosome

Recombinant DNA formed

Another bacterial cell takes up recombinant DNA

Insulin produced

Reproduction

More genetically-engineered cells making insulin

Crop plants are now being genetically engineered to produce chemicals that kill specific pests that feed on them. Some of the pollen from pesticide-resistant canola crops is capable of spreading up to 8 km from the plant, while corn and potato pollen can spread up to 1 km. What might be the effects of pollen landing on other plants?

Recombinant DNA Making recombinant DNA is one method of genetic engineering. Recombinant DNA is made by inserting a useful segment of DNA from one organism into a bacterium, as illustrated in **Figure 12.** Large quantities of human insulin, a substance needed by people with diabetes to control the level of sugar in their blood, are made by organisms that have been genetically engineered. Other uses include the production of growth hormone to treat dwarfism and chemicals to treat cancer.

Gene Therapy Gene therapy is a kind of genetic engineering. In gene therapy, a normal allele is placed in a virus, as shown in **Figure 13.** The virus then delivers the normal allele when it infects its target cell. The normal allele replaces the defective one. Scientists are conducting experiments that use this method to test ways of controlling cystic fibrosis and some kinds of cancer. More than 2,000 people already have taken part in gene therapy experiments. Gene therapy might be a method of curing several other genetic disorders in the future.

Figure 13
Gene therapy involves placing a normal allele in a cell that has a mutation. When the normal allele begins to function, a genetic disorder such as cystic fibrosis (CF) may be corrected.

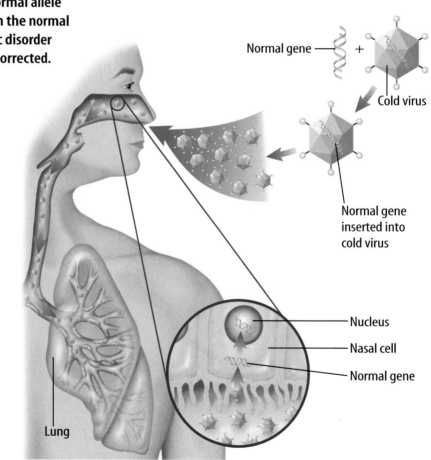

Genetically Engineered Plants For thousands of years people have improved the plants they use for food and clothing even without the knowledge of genotypes. Until recently, these improvements were the results of selecting plants with the most desired traits to bred for the next generation. This process is called selective breeding. Recent advances in genetics have not replaced selective breeding. Although a plant may be bred for a particular phenotype, the genotype and pedigree of the plants also are considered.

Genetic engineering can produce improvements in crop plants, such as corn, wheat, and rice. One type of genetic engineering involves finding the genes that produce desired traits in one plant and then inserting those genes into a different plant. Scientists recently have made genetically engineered tomatoes with a gene that allows tomatoes to be picked green and transported great distances before they ripen completely. Ripe, firm tomatoes are then available in the local market. In the future, additional food crops may be genetically engineered so that they are not desirable food for insects.

Figure 14
Genetically engineered produce is sometimes labeled. This allows consumers to make informed choices about their foods.

✔ **Reading Check** *What other types of traits would be considered desirable in plants?*

Because some people might prefer foods that are not changed genetically, some stores label such produce, as shown in **Figure 14.** The long-term effects of consuming genetically engineered plants are unknown.

Section 3 Assessment

1. Give examples of areas in which advances in genetics are important.
2. Compare and contrast the technologies of using recombinant DNA and gene therapy.
3. What are some benefits of genetically engineered crops?
4. How does selective breeding differ from genetic engineering?
5. **Think Critically** Why might some people be opposed to genetically engineered plants?

Skill Builder Activities

6. **Concept Mapping** Make an events chain concept map of the steps used in making recombinant DNA. **For more help, refer to the** Science Skill Handbook.

7. **Using a Word Processor** Use a computer word processing program to write predictions about how advances in genetics might affect your life in the next ten years. **For more help, refer to the** Technology Skill Handbook.

Tests for Color Blindness

What do color-blind people see? People who have inherited color blindness can see most colors, but they have difficulty telling the difference between two specific colors. You have three genes that help you see color. One gene lets you see red, another blue, and the third gene allows you to see green. In the most common type of color blindness, red-green blindness, the green gene does not work properly. What is the percentage of people who are color-blind?

Recognize the Problem

What percentages of males and females in your school are color-blind?

Form a Hypothesis

Based on your reading and your own experiences, form a hypothesis about how common color blindness is among males and females.

Goals
- **Design** an experiment that tests for a specific type of color blindness in males and females.
- **Calculate** the percentage of males and females with the disorder.

Possible Materials
white paper or poster board
colored markers: red, orange, yellow,
    bright green, dark green, blue
*computer and color printer
*Alternate materials

To a person with red-green blindness, bright green appears tan in color, and dark green looks like brown. The color red also looks brown, making it difficult to tell the different between green and red. A person without red-green color blindness could see a "6" in this test, while a red-green color blind person cannot see this number.

Test Your Hypothesis

Plan

1. Decide what type of color blindness you will test for—the common green-red blindness or the more rare green-blue blindness.

2. **List** the materials you will need and describe how you will create test pictures. Tests for color blindness use many circles of red, orange, and yellow as a background, with circles of dark and light green to make a picture or number. List the steps you will take to test your hypothesis.

3. Prepare a data table in your Science Journal to record your test results.

4. **Examine** your experiment to make sure all steps are in logical order.

5. **Identify** which pictures you will use as a control and which pictures you will use as variables.

Do

1. Make sure your teacher approves your plan before you start.

2. **Draw** the pictures that you will use to test for color blindness.

3. Carry out your experiment as planned and record your results in your data table.

Analyze Your Data

1. **Calculate** the percentage of males and females that tested positive for color blindness.

2. **Compare** the frequency of color blindness in males with the frequency of the color blindness in females.

Draw Conclusions

1. Did the results support your hypothesis? Explain.

2. Use your results to explain why color blindness is called a sex-linked disorder.

3. **Infer** how common the color-blind disorder is in the general population.

4. **Predict** your results if you were to test a larger number of people.

*C*ommunicating
Your Data

Using a word processor, **write** a short article for the advice column of a fashion magazine about how a color-blind person can avoid wearing outfits with clashing colors. **For more help, refer to the** Technology Skill Handbook.

Science Stats

The Human Genome

Did you know...

. . . The human genome is not very different from the genome of mice. As shown to the right, many of the genes that are found on mouse chromosome 17 are similar to genes on human chromosomes. Humans may be more closely related to other organisms than previously thought.

Found on human chromosome

Mouse chromosome 17

6
16
21
6
19
18
2

. . . The strands of DNA in the human genome, if unwound and connected end to end, would be more than 1.5 m long—but only about 130 trillionths of a centimeter wide. Even an average human hair is as much as 200,000 times wider than that.

Human hair

DNA

Centriole

Nucleus

Endoplasmic reticulum

Mitochondrion

Cytoplasm

. . . The biggest advance in genetics in years took place in February, 2001. Scientists successfully mapped the human genome. There are about 30,000 genes in the human genome. Genes are in the nucleus of each of the several trillion cells in your body.

. . . It would take about nine and one-half years to read aloud without stopping the 3 billion bits of instructions (called base pairs) in your genome.

Genome Sizes of Various Organisms

Number of genes (in thousands) — Human, Mouse, Fruit Fly, Fungus, *E. coli* bacteria — Organism

. . . Not all the DNA in your genes contains useful information. About 90 percent of it is "junk" DNA—meaningless sequences located in and between genes.

Do the Math

1. If one million base pairs of DNA take up 1 megabyte of storage space on a computer, how many gigabytes (1,024 megabytes) would the whole genome fill?
2. Consult the above graph. How many more genes are in the human genome than the genome of the fruit fly?
3. If you wrote the genetic information for each gene in the human genome on a separate sheet of 0.2-mm-thick paper and stacked the sheets, how tall would the stack be?

Go Further

By decoding the human genome scientists hope to identify the location of disease-causing genes. Research a genetic disease and share your results with your class.

Chapter 5 Study Guide

Reviewing Main Ideas

Section 1   Genetics

1. Genetics is the study of how traits are inherited. Gregor Mendel determined the basic laws of genetics.

2. Traits are controlled by alleles on chromosomes in the nuclei of cells.

3. Some alleles can be dominant and others can be recessive in action.

4. When a pair of chromosomes separates during meiosis, the different alleles for a trait move into separate sex cells. Mendel found that traits followed the laws of probability and that he could predict the outcome of genetic crosses. *How can a Punnett square help predict inheritance of traits?*

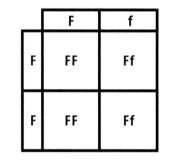

	F	f
F	FF	Ff
F	FF	Ff

Section 2   Genetics Since Mendel

1. Inheritance patterns studied since Mendel include incomplete dominance, multiple alleles, and polygenic inheritance.

2. These inheritance patterns allow a greater variety of phenotypes to be produced than would result from Mendelian inheritance.

3. Some disorders are the results of inheritance and can be harmful, even deadly, to those affected.

4. Pedigree charts help reveal patterns of the inheritance of a trait in a family. Pedigrees show that sex-linked traits are expressed more often in males than in females.

Section 3   Advances in Genetics

1. Genetic engineering uses biological and chemical methods to add or remove genes in an organism's DNA.

2. Recombinant DNA is one way genetic engineering can be performed using bacteria to make useful chemicals, including hormones.

3. Gene therapy shows promise for correcting many human genetic disorders by inserting normal alleles into cells.

4. Breakthroughs in the field of genetic engineering are allowing scientists to do many things, such as producing plants that are resistant to disease. *What types of crops might benefit from advances in genetic engineering? Give examples.*

After You Read

FOLDABLES
Reading & Study Skills

How many characteristics listed in your Classify Study Fold are inherited from your parents? How many are not inherited? Why are some not inherited?

Visualizing Main Ideas

Examine the following pedigree for diabetes and explain the inheritance pattern.

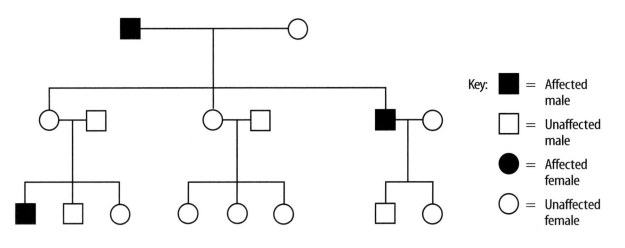

Key:
■ = Affected male
□ = Unaffected male
● = Affected female
○ = Unaffected female

Vocabulary Review

Vocabulary Words

a. allele
b. dominant
c. genetic engineering
d. genetics
e. genotype
f. heredity
g. heterozygous
h. homozygous
i. hybrid
j. incomplete dominance
k. phenotype
l. polygenic inheritance
m. Punnett square
n. recessive
o. sex-linked gene

Using Vocabulary

Make the sentences to the right true by replacing the underlined word with the correct vocabulary word.

Study Tip

When you encounter new vocabulary, write it down in a sentence. This will help you understand, remember, and use new vocabulary words.

1. Alternate forms of a gene are called <u>genetics</u>.

2. The outward appearance of a trait is a <u>genotype</u>.

3. Human height, eye color, and skin color are all traits controlled by <u>sex-linked genes</u>.

4. An allele that produces a trait in the heterozygous condition is <u>recessive</u>.

5. <u>Polygenic inheritance</u> is the branch of biology that deals with the study of heredity.

6. The actual combination of alleles of an organism is its <u>phenotype</u>.

7. <u>Hybrids</u> are moving fragments of DNA from one organism and inserting them into another organism.

8. A <u>phenotype</u> is a helpful device for predicting the proportions of possible genotypes.

9. <u>Genetics</u> is the passing of traits from parents to offspring.

10. Red-green color blindness and hemophilia are two human genetic disorders that are caused by a <u>genotype</u>.

Chapter 5 Assessment

Checking Concepts

Choose the word or phrase that best answers the question.

1. Which of the following are located in the nuclei on chromosomes?
   A) genes
   C) carbohydrates
   B) pedigrees
   D) zygotes

2. Which of the following describes the allele that causes color blindness?
   A) dominant
   B) carried on the Y chromosome
   C) carried on the X chromosome
   D) present only in males

3. What is it called when the presence of two different alleles results in an intermediate phenotype?
   A) incomplete dominance
   B) polygenic inheritance
   C) multiple alleles
   D) sex-linked genes

4. What separates during meiosis?
   A) proteins
   C) alleles
   B) phenotypes
   D) pedigrees

5. What controls traits in organisms?
   A) cell membrane
   C) genes
   B) cell wall
   D) Punnett squares

6. Which of the following is a use for a Punnett square?
   A) to dominate the outcome of a cross
   B) to predict the outcome of a cross
   C) to assure the outcome of a cross
   D) to number the outcome of a cross

7. What term describes the inheritance of cystic fibrosis?
   A) polygenic inheritance
   B) multiple alleles
   C) incomplete dominance
   D) recessive genes

8. What type of inheritance is eye color?
   A) polygenic inheritance
   B) multiple alleles
   C) incomplete dominance
   D) recessive genes

9. What chromosome(s) did the father contribute if a normal female is produced?
   A) X
   C) Y
   B) XX
   D) XY

10. What type of inheritance is blood type?
    A) polygenic inheritance
    B) multiple alleles
    C) incomplete dominance
    D) recessive genes

Thinking Critically

11. Explain the relationship among DNA, genes, alleles, and chromosomes.

12. Explain how the parents and offspring represented in this Punnett square have the same phenotype.

	F	f
F	FF	Ff
F	FF	Ff

13. Explain why two rabbits with the same genes might not be colored the same if one is raised in Maine and one in Texas.

14. Why would a person who receives genetic therapy for a disorder still be able to pass the disorder to his or her children?

Developing Skills

15. **Predicting** Two organisms were found to have different genotypes but have the same phenotype. Predict what these phenotypes might be. Explain.

16. Classifying Classify the inheritance pattern for each of the following:
   a. many different phenotypes produced by one pair of alleles;
   b. many phenotypes produced by more than one pair of alleles; two phenotypes from two alleles; three phenotypes from two alleles.

17. Comparing and Contrasting Compare and contrast Mendelian inheritance with incomplete dominance.

18. Interpreting Scientific Illustrations What were the genotypes of the parents that produced the following Punnett square?

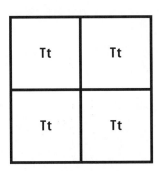

19. Newspaper Article Write a newspaper article to announce a new, genetically engineered plant. Include the method of developing the plant, the characteristic changed, and the terms that you would expect to see. Read your article to the class.

TECHNOLOGY

Go to the Glencoe Science Web site at **science.glencoe.com** or use the **Glencoe Science CD-ROM** for additional chapter assessment.

THE PRINCETON REVIEW **Test Practice**

A scientist is studying pea plants. The scientist made this Punnett square to predict the color traits of the offspring of two parent pea plants.

Parent (Yy)

	Y	y
Y	YY	Yy
y	Yy	??

Parent (Yy)

Study the Punnett square and answer the following questions.

1. Which of these genotypes will complete this Punnett square?
   A) YY
   B) Yy
   C) yy
   D) Yx

2. In peas, the color yellow (Y) is dominant to the color green (y). According to this Punnett square, most of the offspring of the yellow pea plant and the green pea plant probably will be _____.
   F) orange
   G) green
   H) yellow
   J) red

Adaptations Over Time

A re today's cockroaches different from those that lived 10,000 years ago? How have these and other organisms survived Earth's changing environments over time? What evidence exists for changes in a species? Theories about how species change over time and some of the evidence for these changes are presented in this chapter. You also will read about primate adaptations over time.

What do you think?

Science Journal Look at the picture below with a classmate. Discuss what might be happening. Here's a hint: *This is one of the reasons species change.* Write your answer or best guess in your Science Journal.

The cheetah is one of nature's speediest hunters, but it can run swiftly for only short distances. The cheetah's fur blends in with tall grass, making it almost invisible as it hides and waits for prey to wander close by. Then the cheetah pounces, capturing the prey before it can run away.

Model camouflage

1. Spread a sheet of newspaper classified ads on the floor.

2. Using a hole puncher, punch out 100 circles from each of the following types of paper: white paper, black paper, and classified ads.

3. Scatter all the circles on the newspaper on the floor. For 10 s, pick up as many circles as possible, one at a time. Have a partner time you.

4. Count the number of each kind of paper circle that you picked up. Record your results in your Science Journal.

Observe

Which paper circles were most difficult to find? What can you infer about a cheetah's coloring from this activity? Enter your responses to these questions in your Science Journal.

Before You Read

FOLDABLES
Reading & Study Skills

Making a Sequence Study Fold Make the following Foldable to help you predict what might occur next in adaptations over time.

1. Place a sheet of paper in front of you so the long side is at the top. Fold the paper in half from top to bottom.

2. Fold both sides in. Unfold the paper so three sections show.

3. Through the top thickness of paper, cut along each of the fold lines to the top fold, forming three tabs. Label each tab *Past, Present,* and *Future* as shown. Title the middle tab *Primates.*

4. Before you read the chapter, write what primates have in common under the *Present* tab. As you read the chapter, write what primates were like in the past under the *Past* tab.

Ideas About Evolution

What **You'll** **Learn**

- **Describe** Lamarck's theory of acquired characteristics and Darwin's theory of evolution.
- **Identify** why variations in organisms are important.
- **Compare and contrast** gradualism and punctuated equilibrium.

Vocabulary

species
evolution
natural selection
variation
adaptation
gradualism
punctuated equilibrium

Why **It's** **Important**

The theory of evolution suggests why there are differences among living things.

Early Models of Evolution

Millions of species of plants, animals, and other organisms live on Earth today. Do you suppose they are exactly the same as they were when they first appeared—or have any of them changed? A **species** is a group of organisms that share similar characteristics and can reproduce among themselves to produce fertile offspring. The characteristics of a species are inherited when they pass from parent to offspring. Change in these inherited characteristics over time is **evolution. Figure 1** shows how the characteristics of the camel have changed over time.

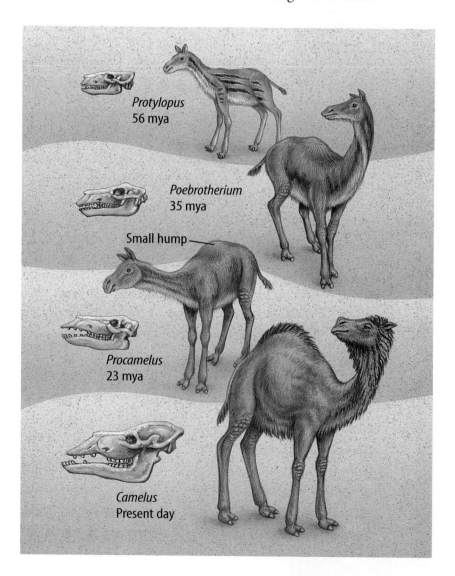

Figure 1

By studying fossils, scientists have traced the evolution of the camel. About 56 million years ago, camels had a small body. Some 33 million years later, species of camels had grown larger and had a small hump. Present-day species are even larger and have a bigger hump.

Theory of Acquired Characteristics In 1809, Jean Baptiste de Lamarck proposed a hypothesis to explain how species change over time. He suggested that characteristics, or traits, developed during a parent organism's lifetime are inherited by its offspring. His hypothesis is called the theory of acquired characteristics. Scientists collected data on traits that are passed from parents to children. The data showed that traits developed during a parent's lifetime, such as large muscles built by hard work or exercise, are not passed on to offspring. The evidence did not support Lamarck's theory.

✓ Reading Check *What was Lamarck's explanation of evolution?*

Darwin's Model of Evolution

In December 1831, the HMS *Beagle* sailed from England on a journey to explore the South American coast. On board was a young naturalist named Charles Darwin. During the journey, Darwin recorded observations about the plants and animals he saw. He was amazed by the variety of life on the Galápagos Islands, which are about 1,000 km from the coast of Ecuador. Darwin hypothesized that the plants and animals on the Galápagos Islands originally must have come from Central and South America. But the islands were home to many species he had not seen in South America, including giant cactus trees, huge land tortoises, and the iguana shown in **Figure 2.**

Figure 2
This map shows the route of Darwin's voyage on the HMS *Beagle*. Darwin noticed many species on the Galápagos Islands that he had not seen along the coast of South America, including the marine iguana. This species is the only lizard in the world known to enter the ocean and feed on seaweed.

Figure 3

Darwin observed that the beak shape of each species of Galápagos finch is related to its eating habits.

A Finches that eat nuts and seeds have short, strong beaks for breaking hard shells.

B Finches that feed on insects have long, slender beaks for probing beneath tree bark.

C Finches with medium-sized beaks eat a variety of foods including seeds and insects.

Research Visit the Glencoe Science Web site at **science.glencoe.com** for more information about the finches Darwin observed. In your Science Journal, describe the similarities and differences of any two species of Galápagos finches.

Darwin's Observations Darwin observed 13 species of finches on the Galápagos Islands. He noticed that all 13 species looked similar, except for differences in body size, beak shape, and eating habits, as shown in **Figure 3.** He also noticed that all the Galápagos finches looked similar to a finch species he had seen on the South American coast. Darwin hypothesized that all 13 Galápagos species evolved from South American species.

Competition and Survival All living organisms produce more offspring than survive. Galápagos finches lay several eggs every few months. Darwin realized that, in just a few years, several pairs of finches could produce a large population. A population is made up of all the individuals of a species living in the same area. Members of a large population compete for living space, food, and other resources. Those that are best able to survive are more likely to reproduce and pass on their traits to the next generation.

Darwin reasoned that the Galápagos finches must have had to compete for food. Finches with beak shapes that allowed them to eat available food survived longer and produced more offspring than finches without those beak shapes. After many generations, these groups of finches became separate species.

✓ **Reading Check** *How did Darwin explain the evolution of the different species of Galápagos finches?*

Natural Selection

After the voyage, Charles Darwin returned to England and continued to think about his observations. He collected more evidence on inherited traits by breeding racing pigeons. He also studied breeds of dogs and varieties of flowers. In the mid 1800s, Darwin developed the theory of evolution that is accepted by most scientists today. He described his ideas in a book called *On the Origin of Species*, which was published in 1859.

Darwin's observations led many other scientists to conduct experiments on inherited characteristics. After many years, Darwin's hypothesis became known as the theory of evolution by natural selection. **Natural selection** means that organisms with traits best suited to their environment are more likely to survive and reproduce. Their traits are passed on to more offspring. The principles that describe how natural selection works are listed in **Table 1.**

Over time, as new data has been gathered and reported, some changes have been made to Darwin's original ideas about evolution by natural selection. His theory remains one of the most important ideas in the study of life science.

Table 1 The Principles of Natural Selection

1. Organisms produce more offspring than can survive.

2. Differences, or variations, occur among individuals of a species.

3. Variations are passed on to offspring.

4. Some variations are helpful. Individuals with helpful variations survive and reproduce better than those without these variations.

5. Over time, the offspring of individuals with helpful variations make up more of a population and eventually become a separate species.

Problem-Solving Activity

Does natural selection take place in a fish tank?

Alejandro raises tropical fish as a hobby. Could the observations that he makes over several weeks illustrate the principles of natural selection?

Identifying the Problem

Alejandro keeps a detailed journal of his observations, some of which are given in the table to the right.

Solving the Problem

Refer to **Table 1** and match each of Alejandro's journal entries with the principle(s) it demonstrates. Here's a hint: *Some entries may not match any of the principles of natural selection. Some entries may match more than one principle.*

Fish Tank Observations

Date	Observation
June 6	6 fish are placed in aquarium tank.
July 22	16 new young appear.
July 24	3 young have short or missing tail fins. 13 young have normal tail fins.
July 28	Young with short or missing tail fins die.
August 1	2 normal fish die—from overcrowding?
August 12	30 new young appear.
August 15	5 young have short or missing tail fins. 5 have normal tail fins.
August 18	Young with short or missing tail fins die.
August 20	Tank is overcrowded. Fish are divided equally into two tanks.

Variation and Adaptation

Darwin's theory of natural selection emphasizes the differences among individuals of a species. These differences are called variations. A **variation** is an inherited trait that makes an individual different from other members of its species. Variations result from permanent changes, or mutations, in an organism's genes. Some gene changes produce small variations, such as differences in the shape of human hairlines. Other gene changes produce large variations, such as an albino squirrel in a population of gray squirrels or fruit without seeds. Over time, more and more individuals of the species might inherit these variations. If individuals with these variations continue to survive and reproduce over many generations, a new species can evolve. It might take hundreds, thousands, or millions of generations for a new species to evolve.

Some variations are more helpful than others. An **adaptation** is any variation that makes an organism better suited to its environment. The variations that result in an adaptation can involve an organism's color, shape, behavior, or chemical makeup. Camouflage (KA muh flahj) is an adaptation. A camouflaged organism, like the one shown in **Figure 4,** blends into its environment and is more likely to survive and reproduce.

Figure 4
Variations that provide an advantage tend to increase in a population over time. Variations that result in a disadvantage tend to decrease in a population over time.

A Camouflage allows organisms to blend into their environment. *How does its coloration give this scorpion fish a survival advantage?*

B Albinism can prevent an organism from blending into its environment. *What might happen to an albino lemur in its natural environment?*

Figure 5
About 600 years ago, European rabbits were introduced to the Canary Islands from a visiting Portuguese ship. The Canary Islands are in the Atlantic Ocean off the northwest coast of Africa. Over time, the Canary Island rabbits became a separate species.

A European rabbits feed during the day and are fairly large.

B Canary Island rabbits feed during the night. *Why might large eyes be considered a helpful adaptation in Canary Island rabbits?*

Changes in the Sources of Gene
Over time, the genetic makeup of a species might change its appearance. For example, as the genetic makeup of a species of seed-eating Galápagos finch changes, so does the size and shape of its beak. Many kinds of environmental factors help bring about changes. When individuals of the same species move in to or out of an area, they might bring in or remove genes and variations. Suppose a family from another country moves to your neighborhood. They bring with them different foods, customs, and ways of speaking. In a similar way, when new individuals enter an existing population, they can bring in different genes and variations.

Geographic Isolation
Sometimes mountains, lakes, or other geologic features isolate a small number of individuals from the rest of a population. Over several generations, variations that do not exist in the larger population might begin to be more common in the isolated population. Also, gene mutations can occur that add variations to populations. Over time, the two populations can become so different that they no longer breed with each other. The two populations of rabbits shown in **Figure 5** have been isolated from each other geographically for thousands of generations.

Relating Evolution to Species

Procedure
1. On a piece of **lined paper,** print the alphabet in lowercase letters.
2. Organize the letters into three groups. Put all of the vowels in the first group. Place all of the letters that drop below the line into the second group. Place all of the remaining letters in the third group.

Analysis
1. How are the three groups of letters similar to each other?
2. If the letters were organisms, what traits would indicate to scientists how closely related the letters were to each other?

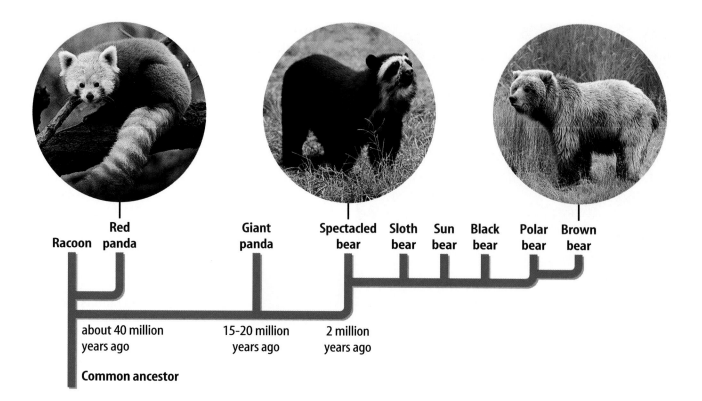

about 40 million years ago

15-20 million years ago

2 million years ago

Common ancestor

Racoon Red panda Giant panda Spectacled bear Sloth bear Sun bear Black bear Polar bear Brown bear

Figure 6
The evolution of bears illustrates the punctuated equilibrium model of evolution. Six distinct bear species evolved over two million years. The same series of changes would have taken many times longer according to the gradualism model of evolution.

The Speed of Evolution

Scientists do not agree on how quickly evolution occurs. Many scientists hypothesize that evolution occurs slowly, perhaps over tens or hundreds of millions of years. Other scientists hypothesize that evolution can occur quickly. Some scientists propose that evidence supports both of these models.

Gradualism Darwin hypothesized that evolution takes place slowly. The model that describes evolution as a slow, ongoing process by which one species changes to a new species is known as **gradualism.** According to the gradualism model, a continuing series of mutations and variations over time will result in a new species. Look back at **Figure 1,** which shows the evolution of the camel over tens of millions of years. Fossil evidence shows a series of intermediate forms that indicate a gradual change from the earliest camel species to today's species.

Punctuated Equilibrium Gradualism doesn't explain the evolution of all species. For some species, the fossil record shows few intermediate forms—one species suddenly changes to another. According to the **punctuated equilibrium** model, rapid evolution comes about when the mutation of a few genes results in the appearance of a new species over a relatively short period of time. The fossil record gives examples of this type of evolution, as you can see in **Figure 6.**

Punctuated Equilibrium Today Evolution by the punctuated equilibrium model can occur over a few thousand or million years, and sometimes even faster. For example, many bacteria have changed in a few decades. The antibiotic penicillin originally came from the fungus shown in **Figure 7.** But many bacteria species that were once easily killed by penicillin no longer are harmed by it. These bacteria have developed resistance to the drug. Penicillin has been in use since 1943. Just four years later, in 1947, a species of bacteria that causes pneumonia and other infections already had developed resistance to the drug. By the 1990s, several disease-producing bacteria had become resistant to penicillin and many other antibiotics.

How did penicillin-resistant bacteria evolve so quickly? As in any population, some organisms have variations that allow them to survive unfavorable living conditions when other organisms cannot. When penicillin was used to kill bacteria, those with the penicillin-resistant variation survived, reproduced, and passed this trait to their offspring. Over a period of time, this bacteria population became penicillin-resistant.

Figure 7
The fungus growing in this petri dish is *Penicillium*, the original source of penicillin. It produces an antibiotic substance that prevents the growth of certain bacteria.

Section 1 Assessment

1. Compare Lamarck's and Darwin's ideas about how evolution takes place.

2. Explain why variations are important to the survival of a population.

3. Explain how the gradualism model of evolution differs from the punctuated equilibrium model of evolution.

4. How does geographic isolation contribute to evolution?

5. **Think Critically** What adaptations would be helpful for an animal species that was moved to the arctic?

Skill Builder Activities

6. **Concept Mapping** Use information given in **Figure 6** to make a concept map that shows how raccoons, red pandas, giant pandas, polar bears, and black bears are related to a common ancestor. **For more help,** refer to the Science Skill Handbook.

7. **Using Percentages** The evolution of the camel can be traced back at least 56 million years. Use **Figure 1** to estimate the percent of this time that the modern camel has existed. **For more help,** refer to the Math Skill Handbook.

Activity

Hidden Frogs

Through natural selection, animals become adapted for survival in their environment. Adaptations include shapes, colors, and even textures that help an animal blend into its surroundings. These adaptations are called camouflage. The red-eyed tree frog's mint green body blends in with tropical forest vegetation as shown in the photo on the right. Could you design camouflage for a desert frog? A temperate forest frog?

What You'll Investigate

What type of camouflage would best suit a frog living in a particular habitat?

Materials (for each group)

cardboard form of a frog   glue
colored markers   beads
crayons   sequins
colored pencils   modeling clay

Goals

■ **Create** a frog model camouflaged to blend in with its surroundings.

Safety Precautions 🥽

Procedure

1. Choose one of the following habitats for your frog model: muddy shore of a pond, orchid flowers in a tropical rain forest, multicolored clay in a desert, or the leaves and branches of trees in a temperate forest.

2. **List** the features of your chosen habitat that will determine the camouflage your frog model will need.

3. **Brainstorm** with your group the body shape, coloring, and skin texture that would make the best camouflage for your model. Record your ideas in your Science Journal.

4. **Draw** samples of colors, patterns, texture, and other features your frog model might have in your Science Journal.

5. Show your design ideas to your teacher and ask for further input.

6. **Construct** your frog model.

Conclude and Apply

1. **Explain** how the characteristics of the habitat helped you decide on the specific frog features you chose.

2. **Infer** how the color patterns and other physical features of real frogs develop in nature.

3. **Explain** why it might be harmful to release a frog into a habitat for which it is not adapted.

Communicating Your Data

Create a poster or other visual display that represents the habitat you chose for this activity. Use your display to show classmates how your design helps camouflage your frog model. **For more help, refer to the** Science Skill Handbook.

Clues About Evolution

Clues from Fossils

Imagine going on a fossil hunt in Wyoming. Your companions are paleontologists—scientists who study the past by collecting and examining fossils. As you climb a low hill, you notice a curved piece of stone jutting out of the sandy soil. One of the paleontologists carefully brushes the soil away and congratulates you on your find. You've discovered part of the fossilized shell of a turtle like the one shown in **Figure 8.**

The Green River Formation covers parts of Wyoming, Utah, and Colorado. On your fossil hunt, you learn that about 50 million years ago, during the Eocene Epoch, this region was covered by lakes. The water was home to fish, crocodiles, lizards, and turtles. Palms, fig trees, willows, and cattails grew on the lakeshores. Insects and birds flew through the air. How do scientists know all this? After many of the plants and animals of that time died, they were covered with silt and mud. Over millions of years, they became the fossils that have made the Green River Formation one of the richest fossil deposits in the world.

As You Read

What **You'll Learn**

- **Identify** the importance of fossils as evidence of evolution.
- **Explain** how relative and radiometric dating are used to estimate the age of fossils.
- **List** examples of five types of evidence for evolution.

Vocabulary

sedimentary rock
radioactive element
embryology
homologous
vestigial structure

Why **It's Important**

The scientific evidence for evolution helps you understand why this theory is so important to the study of biology.

The turtle *Cisternum undatum* is from the same fossil formation.

The most abundant fossils are of a fresh-water herring, *Knightia oecaena,* which is Wyoming's state fossil.

Figure 8
The desert of the Green River Formation is home to prong-horn antelope, elks, coyotes, and eagles. Fossil evidence shows that about 50 million years ago the environment was much warmer and wetter than it is today.

Figure 9

Examples of several different types of fossils are shown here. *Which of these would most likely be found in a layer of sedimentary rock?*

B **Mineralized fossils** Minerals can replace wood or bone to create a piece of petrified wood shown to the left or a mineralized bone fossil.

A **Imprint fossils** A leaf, feather, bones, or even the entire body of an organism can leave an imprint on sediment that later hardens to become rock.

C **Frozen fossils** The remains of organisms like this mammoth can be trapped in ice that remains frozen for thousands or millions of years.

E **Cast Fossils** Minerals can fill in the hollows of animal tracks as shown to the right, mollusk shell, or other parts of an organism to create a cast.

D **Fossils in amber** When the sticky resin of certain cone-bearing plants hardens over time, amber forms. It can contain the remains of trapped insects.

Types of Fossils

Earth Science INTEGRATION

Most of the evidence for evolution comes from fossils. A fossil is the remains, an imprint, or a trace of a prehistoric organism. Several types of fossils are shown in **Figure 9.** Most fossils are found in sedimentary rock. **Sedimentary rock** is formed when layers of sand, silt, clay, or mud are compacted and cemented together, or when minerals are deposited from a solution. Limestone, sandstone, and shale are all examples of sedimentary rock. Fossils are found more often in limestone than in any other kind of sedimentary rock. The fossil record provides evidence that living things have evolved. Other areas of study in addition to fossils also support the theory of evolution.

Determining a Fossil's Age

Paleontologists use detective skills to determine the age of dinosaur fossils or the remains of other ancient organisms. They can use clues provided by unique rock layers and the fossils they contain. The clues provide information about the geology, weather, and life-forms that must have been present during each geologic time period. Two basic methods—relative dating and radiometric dating—can be used, alone or together, to estimate the ages of rocks and fossils.

Relative Dating
One way to find the approximate age of fossils found within a rock layer is relative dating. Relative dating is based on the idea that in undisturbed areas, younger rock layers are deposited on top of older rock layers, as shown in **Figure 10.** Relative dating provides only an estimate of a fossil's age. The estimate is made by comparing the ages of rock layers found above and below the fossil layer. For example, suppose a 50-million-year-old rock layer lies below a fossil, and a 35-million-year-old layer lies above it. According to relative dating, the fossil is probably between 35 million and 50 million years old.

✔ **Reading Check**   *Why can relative dating be used only to estimate the age of a fossil?*

Radiometric Dating
Scientists can obtain a more accurate estimate of the age of a rock layer by using radioactive elements. A **radioactive element** gives off a steady amount of radiation as it slowly changes to a nonradioactive element. Each radioactive element gives off radiation at a different rate. Scientists can estimate the age of the rock by comparing the amount of radioactive element with the amount of nonradioactive element in the rock. This method of dating does not always produce exact results, because the original amount of radioactive element in the rock can never be determined for certain.

SCIENCE
Online

Data Update Visit the Glencoe Science Web site at **science.glencoe.com** for news about recent fossil discoveries. In your Science Journal, write a brief report describing how one of these discoveries was made and what it reveals about past life on Earth.

Figure 10
In Bryce Canyon, erosion by water and wind has cut through the sedimentary rock, exposing the layers. Fossils found in lower layers of sedimentary rock are usually older than the fossils found in upper layers.

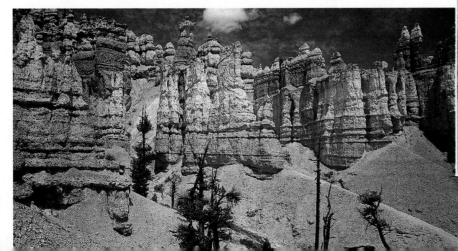

Figure 11

Earth is roughly 4.6 billion years old. As shown here, the vast period of time from Earth's beginning to the present day has been organized into the geologic time scale. The scale is divided into eras and periods. Dates on this scale are given as millions of years ago (mya).

Fossils and Evolution

Fossils provide a record of organisms that lived in the past. However, the fossil record has gaps, much like a book with pages missing. The gaps exist because of an incomplete rock record and most organisms do not become fossils. This means that the fossil record will always be incomplete. By looking at fossils, scientists conclude that many simpler forms of life existed earlier in Earth's history, and more complex forms of life appeared later, as shown in **Figure 11.** Fossils provide direct evidence that evolution has occurred on Earth.

Almost every week, fossil discoveries are made somewhere in the world. When fossils are found, they are used to help scientists understand the past. Scientists can use fossils to make models that show what the organisms could have looked like. From fossils, scientists can sometimes determine whether the organisms lived in family groups or alone, what they ate, what kind of environment they lived in, and many other things about them. Most fossils represent extinct organisms. From a study of the fossil record, scientists have concluded that more than 99 percent of all organisms that have ever existed are extinct now.

More Clues About Evolution

Besides fossils, what other clues do humans have about evolution? Sometimes, evolution can be directly observed. Plant breeders observe evolution when they use cross-breeding to produce genetic changes in plants. The development of antibiotic resistance in bacteria is another direct observation of evolution. Entomologists have noted similar rapid evolution of pesticide-resistant insect species. These observations provide direct evidence that evolution occurs. Also, many examples of indirect evidence for evolution exist. They include similarities in embryo structures, the chemical makeup of organisms, including DNA, and the way organisms develop into adults. Indirect evidence does not provide proof of evolution, but it does support the idea that evolution takes place over time.

Embryology The study of embryos and their development is called **embryology** (em bree AH luh jee). An embryo is the earliest growth stage of an organism. A tail and gills or gill slits are found in the embryos of fish, reptiles, birds, and mammals, as **Figure 12** shows. Fish keep their gills, but the other organisms lose them as their development continues. Fish, birds, and reptiles keep their tails, but many mammals lose theirs. These similarities suggest an evolutionary relationship among all vertebrate species.

Earth Science
INTEGRATION

Many organisms have a history that has been preserved in sedimentary rock. Fossils show that the bones of animals such as horses and whales have become reduced in size or number over geologic time, as the species has evolved. In your Science Journal, explain what information can be gathered from changes in structures that occur over time.

Figure 12
Similarities in the embryos of fish, chickens, and rabbits show evidence of evolution.

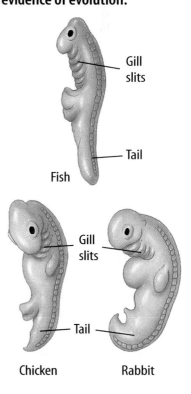

Gill slits

Tail

Fish

Gill slits

Tail

Chicken   Rabbit

Porpoise flipper   Frog forelimb   Human arm   Bat wing

Figure 13
A porpoise flipper, frog forelimb, human arm, and bat wing are homologous. These structures show different arrangements and shapes of the bones of the forelimb. They have the same number of bones, muscles, and blood vessels, and they developed from similar tissues.

Homologous Structures What do the structures shown in **Figure 13** have in common? Although they have different functions, each of these structures is made up of the same kind of bones. Body parts that are similar in origin and structure are called **homologous** (hoh MAH luh gus). Homologous structures also can be similar in function. They often indicate that two or more species share common ancestors.

☑ **Reading Check** *What do homologous structures indicate?*

Vestigial Structures The bodies of some organisms include **vestigial** (veh STIH jee ul) **structures**—structures that don't seem to have a function. Vestigial structures also provide evidence for evolution. For example, manatees, snakes, and whales no longer have back legs, but, like all animals with legs, they still have pelvic bones. The human appendix is a vestigial structure. The appendix appears to be a small version of the cecum, which is an important part of the digestive tract of many mammals. Scientists hypothesize that vestigial structures, like those shown in **Figure 14**, are body parts that once functioned in an ancestor.

Figure 14
Humans have three small muscles around each ear that are vestigial. In some mammals, such as horses, these muscles are large. They allow a horse to turn its ears toward the source of a sound. Humans cannot rotate their ears, but some people can wiggle their ears.

DNA If you enjoy science fiction, you probably have read books or seen movies in which scientists re-create dinosaurs and other extinct organisms from DNA taken from fossils. DNA is the molecule that controls heredity and directs the development of every organism. In a cell with a nucleus, DNA is found in genes that make up the chromosomes. Scientists compare DNA from living organisms to identify similarities among species. Examinations of ancient DNA often provide additional evidence of how some species evolved from their extinct ancestors. By looking at DNA, scientists also can determine how closely related organisms are. For example, DNA studies indicate that dogs are the closest relatives of bears.

Figure 15
Gorillas have DNA and proteins that are similar to humans and other primates.

Similar DNA also can suggest common ancestry. Apes such as the gorillas shown in **Figure 15,** chimpanzees, and orangutans, have 24 pairs of chromosomes. Humans have 23 pairs. When two of an ape's chromosomes are laid end to end, a match for human chromosome number 2 is formed. Also, similar proteins such as hemoglobin—the oxygen-carrying protein in red blood cells—are found in many primates. This can be further evidence that primates have a common ancestor.

Section 2 Assessment

1. How are relative dating and radiometric dating used by scientists?

2. Why are fossils important evidence of evolution? Describe five different kinds of fossils.

3. Explain how DNA can provide some evidence of evolution.

4. Describe three examples of direct evidence for evolution.

5. **Think Critically** Compare and contrast the five types of evidence that support the theory of evolution.

Skill Builder Activities

6. **Interpreting Scientific Illustrations** According to **Figure 11,** what was the longest geological era? What was the shortest era? During what period did mammals appear? **For more help, refer to the** Science Skill Handbook.

7. **Using Percentages** The Cenozoic Era represents about 66 million years. Approximately what percent of Earth's 4.6-billion-year history does this era represent? **For more help, refer to the** Math Skill Handbook.

The Evolution of Primates

As You Read

What You'll Learn

- **Describe** the differences among living primates.
- **Identify** the adaptations of primates.
- **Discuss** the evolutionary history of modern primates.

Vocabulary

primate
hominid
Homo sapiens

Why It's Important

Studying primate evolution will help you appreciate the differences among primates.

Figure 16
The ability to rotate the shoulder in a complete circle allows humans to swim through water and tree-dwelling primates to travel through treetops.

Primates

Humans, monkeys, and apes belong to the group of mammals known as the **primates.** All primates have opposable thumbs, binocular vision, and flexible shoulders that allow the arms to rotate. These shared characteristics could indicate that all primates may have evolved from a common ancestor.

Having an opposable thumb allows you to cross your thumb over your palm and touch your fingers. This means that you can grasp and hold things with your hands. An opposable thumb allows tree-dwelling primates to hold on to branches.

Binocular vision permits you to judge depth or distance with your eyes. In a similar way, it allows tree-dwelling primates to judge the distances as they move between branches. Flexible shoulders and rotating forelimbs also help tree-dwelling primates move from branch to branch. They also allow humans to do the backstroke, as shown in **Figure 16.**

Primates are divided into two major groups. The first group, the prosimians (pro SIH mee uhn), includes lemurs and tarsiers like those shown in **Figure 17.** The second group, anthropoids (AN thruh poydz), includes monkeys, apes, and humans.

Figure 17
Tarsiers and lemurs are active at night.
A Tarsiers are commonly found in the rain forests of Southeast Asia.
B Lemurs live on Madagascar and other nearby islands.

Hominids About 4 million to 6 million years ago, humanlike primates appeared that were different from the other primates. These ancestors, called **hominids,** ate both meat and plants and walked upright on two legs. Hominids shared some characteristics with gorillas, orangutans, and chimpanzees, but a larger brain separated them from the apes.

African Origins In the early 1920s, a fossil skull was discovered in a quarry in South Africa. The skull had a small space for the brain, but it had a humanlike jaw and teeth. The fossil, named *Australopithecus,* was one of the oldest hominids discovered. An almost-complete skeleton of *Australopithecus* was found in northern Africa in 1974. This hominid fossil, shown in **Figure 18,** was called Lucy and had a small brain but is thought to have walked upright. This fossil indicates that modern hominids might have evolved from similar ancestors.

Figure 18
The fossil remains of Lucy are estimated to be 2.9 million to 3.4 million years old.

TRY AT HOME

Mini LAB

Living Without Thumbs

Procedure

1. Using **tape,** fasten down each of your thumbs next to the palm of each hand.
2. Leave your thumbs taped down for at least 1 h. During this time, do the following activities: eat a meal, change clothes, and brush your teeth. Be careful not to try anything that could be dangerous.
3. Untape your thumbs, then write about your experiences in your **Science Journal.**

Analysis

1. Did not having use of your thumbs significantly affect the way you did anything? Explain.
2. Infer how having opposable thumbs could have influenced primate evolution.

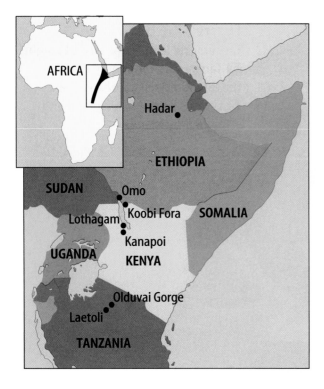

Figure 19
Many of the oldest humanlike skeletons have been found in this area of east Africa.

Early Humans In the 1960s in the region of Africa shown in **Figure 19,** a hominid fossil, which was more like present-day humans than *Australopithecus,* was discovered. The hominid was named *Homo habilis,* the handy man, because simple stone tools were found near him. *Homo habilis* is estimated to be 1.5 million to 2 million years old. Based upon many fossil comparisons, scientists have suggested that *Homo habilis* gave rise to another species, *Homo erectus,* about 1.6 million years ago. This hominid had a larger brain than *Homo habilis. Homo erectus* traveled from Africa to Southeast Asia, China, and possibly Europe. *Homo habilis* and *Homo erectus* are thought to be ancestors of humans because they had larger brains and more humanlike features than *Australopithecus.*

✓ Reading Check *Why was* **Homo habilis** *given that name?*

Humans

The fossil record indicates that *Homo sapiens* evolved about 400,000 years ago. By about 125,000 years ago, two early human groups, Neanderthals and Cro-Magnon humans, as shown in **Figure 20,** probably lived at the same time in parts of Africa and Europe.

Neanderthals Short, heavy bodies with thick bones, small chins, and heavy browridges were physical characteristics of Neanderthals (nee AN dur tawlz). They lived in family groups in caves and used well-made stone tools to hunt large animals. Neanderthals disappeared from the fossil record about 30,000 years ago. They might represent a side branch of human evolution and are not direct ancestors of modern humans.

Figure 20
The skull of a Neanderthal can be compared with the skull of a Cro-Magnon *What differences can you see between these two skulls?*

Skull of a
Neanderthal

Skull of a
Cro-Magnon

Cro-Magnon Humans Cro-Magnon fossils have been found in Europe, Asia, and Australia and date from 10,000 to about 40,000 years in age. Standing about 1.6 m to 1.7 m tall, the physical appearance of Cro-Magnon people was almost the same as that of modern humans. They lived in caves, made stone carvings, and buried their dead. As shown in **Figure 21,** the oldest recorded art has been found on the walls of caves in France, where Cro-Magnon humans first painted bison, horses, and people carrying spears. Cro-Magnon humans are thought to be direct ancestors of early humans, *Homo sapiens,* which means "wise human." Evidence indicates that modern humans, *Homo sapiens sapiens,* evolved from *Homo sapiens.*

Section 3 Assessment

1. Describe at least three kinds of evidence that suggest all primates might have shared a common ancestor.

2. What is the importance of *Australopithecus?*

3. Describe the differences and similarities among Neanderthals, Cro-Magnon humans, and early humans.

4. Which group do most scientists consider to be direct ancestors of modern humans?

5. **Think Critically** Propose a hypothesis about why teeth are the most abundant fossils of hominids.

Skill Builder Activities

6. **Concept Mapping** Make a concept map to show in what sequence the different groups of hominids appeared. Use the following terms: *Homo sapiens sapiens,* Neanderthal, *Homo habilis, Australopithecus, Homo sapiens,* and Cro-Magnon human. **For more help, refer to the** Science Skill Handbook.

7. **Communicating** Write a story in your Science Journal about what life would be like for you if you did not have thumbs. **For more help, refer to the** Science Skill Handbook.

Recognizing Variation in a Population

When you first observe a flock of pigeons, you might think all the birds look alike. However, if you look closer, you will notice minor differences, or variations, among the individuals. Different pigeons might have different color markings, or some might be smaller or larger than others. Individuals of the same species—whether they're birds, plants, or worms—might look alike at first, but some variations undoubtedly exist. According to the principles of natural selection, evolution could not occur without variations. What kinds of variations have you noticed among species of plants or animals?

Recognize the Problem

How can you measure variation in a plant or animal population?

Form a Hypothesis

Make a hypothesis about the amount of variation in the fruit and seeds of one species of plant.

Possible Materials
fruit and seeds from one plant species
metric ruler
magnifying glass
graph paper

Goals
- **Design** an experiment that will allow you to collect data about variation in a population.
- **Observe, measure, and analyze** variations in a population.

Safety Precautions

Do not put any fruit or seeds in your mouth. Wash your hands after handling plant parts.

Test Your Hypothesis

Plan

1. As a group, agree upon and write out the hypothesis statement.

2. **List** the steps you need to take to test your hypothesis. Be specific. Describe exactly what you will do at each step. List your materials.

3. **Decide** what characteristic of fruit and seeds you will study. For example, you could measure the length of fruit and seeds or count the number of seeds per fruit.

4. **Design** a data table in your Science Journal to collect data about two variations. Use the table to record the data your group collects as you complete the experiment.

5. **Identify** any constants, variables, and controls of the experiment.

6. How many fruit and seeds will you examine? Will your data be more accurate if you examine larger numbers?

7. **Summarize** your data in a graph or chart.

Do

1. Make sure your teacher approves your plan before you start.

2. Carry out the experiment as planned.

3. While the experiment is going on, write down any observations you make and complete the data table in your Science Journal.

Analyze Your Data

1. **Calculate** the mean and range of variation in your experiment. The range is the difference between the largest and the smallest measurements. The mean is the sum of all the data divided by the sample size.

2. **Graph** your group's results by making a line graph for the variations you measured. Place the range of variation on the *x*-axis and the number of organisms that had that measurement on the *y*-axis.

Draw Conclusions

1. **Explain** your results in terms of natural selection.

2. What factors did you use to determine the amount of variation present?

3. Suggest reasons why one or more of the variations you observed in this activity might be helpful to the survival of the individual.

*C*ommunicating Your Data

Create a poster or other exhibit that illustrates the variations you and your classmates observed.

Wong-Staal was on one of the two teams that first identified HIV as the virus that causes AIDS.

Fighting

Some people wear a red ribbon as a reminder to fight HIV and AIDS.

The first cases of AIDS, or acquired immune deficiency syndrome, in humans were reported in the early 1980s. AIDS is caused by the human immunodeficiency virus, or HIV. It is most likely that HIV first occurred in nonhuman primates, evolving into a form that could infect humans. For the first two decades of the battle against HIV and AIDS, it looked like the virus might win. Teams of scientists from many fields, and in many parts of the world, are part of the ongoing counterattack.

A major problem in AIDS research is the rapid evolution of HIV. When HIV multiplies inside a host cell, new versions of the virus are produced as well as identical copies of the virus that invaded the cell. New versions of the virus can soon outnumber the original version. That's why HIV is so hard to fight—a treatment that works against today's HIV might not work against tomorrow's version.

These rapid changes in HIV also mean that different strains of the virus exist in different places around the world. That means most vaccines, which are still in the experimental stage, and treatments developed in the United States work only for AIDS patients who contracted the virus in the United States. This leaves AIDS sufferers in some parts of the world without effective treatments. Also, treatments might work for only a short period of time. Traditional vaccines quickly become useless. So, researchers such as geneticist Flossie Wong-Staal at the University of California in San Diego, must look for new ways to fight the evolving virus.

Working Backwards

Flossie Wong-Staal is taking a new approach. Her research focuses on how HIV uses host human cells. First, her team identifies the parts of a human cell that HIV depends on. Next, the team looks for parts of the human cell that HIV needs but the human cell doesn't need. Then the team looks for a way to remove—or inactivate—that unneeded part. This technique limits the virus's ability to multiply.

Wong-Staal's research combines three important aspects of science—a deep understanding of how cells and genes operate, great skill in the techniques of genetics, and great ideas. Understanding, skill, and great ideas are the best weapons so far in the fight to conquer HIV.

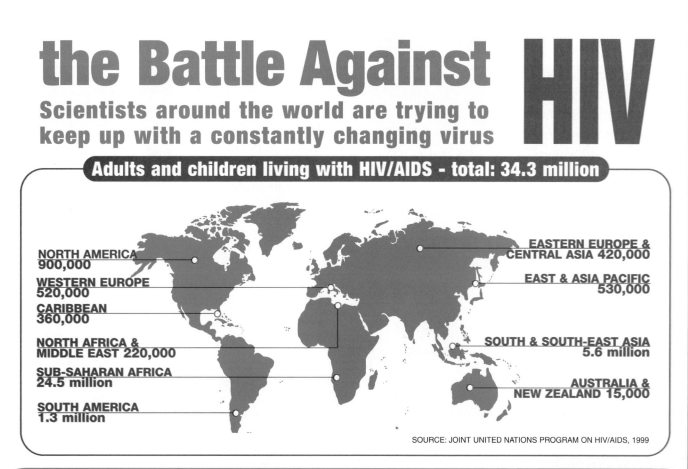

the Battle Against HIV

Scientists around the world are trying to keep up with a constantly changing virus

Adults and children living with HIV/AIDS - total: 34.3 million

NORTH AMERICA 900,000

WESTERN EUROPE 520,000

CARIBBEAN 360,000

NORTH AFRICA & MIDDLE EAST 220,000

SUB-SAHARAN AFRICA 24.5 million

SOUTH AMERICA 1.3 million

EASTERN EUROPE & CENTRAL ASIA 420,000

EAST & ASIA PACIFIC 530,000

SOUTH & SOUTH-EAST ASIA 5.6 million

AUSTRALIA & NEW ZEALAND 15,000

SOURCE: JOINT UNITED NATIONS PROGRAM ON HIV/AIDS, 1999

CONNECTIONS Research Use the Glencoe Science Web site and other sources to determine which nations have the highest rates of AIDS infection. Which nation has the highest rate? Where does the U.S. rank? Next, find data from ten years ago. Have the rankings changed?

SCIENCE *Online*

For more information, visit science.glencoe.com

Reviewing Main Ideas

Section 1 Ideas About Evolution

1. Evolution is one of the central ideas of biology. It is an explanation of how living things have changed in the past and a basis for predicting how they might change in the future.

2. Charles Darwin developed the theory of evolution by natural selection to explain how evolutionary changes account for the diversity of organisms on Earth.

3. Natural selection includes concepts of variation, overproduction, and competition.

4. According to natural selection, organisms with traits best suited to their environment are more likely to survive and reproduce. *What traits make this organism suited to its watery environment?*

Section 2 Clues About Evolution

1. Fossils provide evidence for evolution. *How are imprint fossils like the ones to the right formed?*

2. Relative dating and radiometric dating can be used to estimate the age of fossils.

3. The evolution of antibiotic-resistant bacteria, pesticide-resistant insects, and rapid genetic changes in plant species provide direct evidence that evolution occurs.

4. Homologous structures, vestigial structures, comparative embryology, and chemical similarities in DNA and other substances provide indirect evidence of evolution. *How does DNA provide evidence of evolution?*

Section 3 The Evolution of Primates

1. Primates include monkeys, apes, and humans. Hominids are humanlike primates. *What are the common characteristics of primates?*

2. The earliest known hominid fossil is *Australopithecus.*

3. *Homo sapiens* are thought to have evolved from Cro-Magnon humans at least 400,000 years ago.

FOLDABLES
Reading & Study Skills

After You Read

Using what you learned, predict how primates might change and write your ideas under the *Future* tab of your Foldable.

Visualizing Main Ideas

Complete the following spider map on evolution.

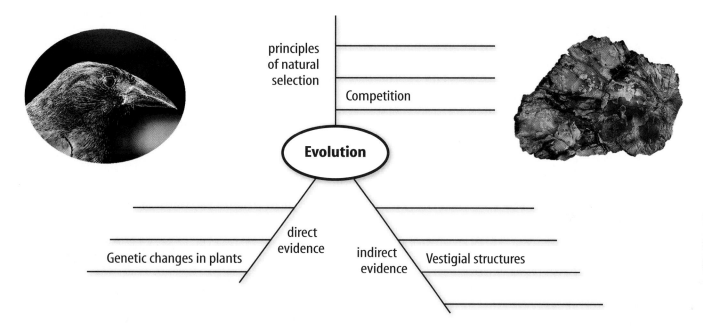

principles
of natural
selection

Competition

Evolution

direct
evidence

Genetic changes in plants

indirect
evidence

Vestigial structures

Vocabulary Review

Vocabulary Words

a. adaptation
b. embryology
c. evolution
d. gradualism
e. hominid
f. *Homo sapiens*
g. homologous
h. natural selection
i. primate

j. punctuated equilibrium
k. radioactive element
l. sedimentary rock
m. species
n. variation
o. vestigial structure

Using Vocabulary

Replace each underlined phrase with the correct vocabulary words.

1. <u>Layers of deposition</u> might contain many different kinds of fossils.

2. The muscles that move the human ear appear to be <u>of no obvious use</u>.

3. Forelimbs of bats, humans, and seals are <u>similar in origin</u>.

4. Opposable thumbs are a characteristic of <u>this group of mammals</u>.

5. The study of <u>early development of species</u> can provide evidence of evolution.

6. The principles of <u>this mechanism of evolution</u> include variation and competition.

7. <u>Early humans</u> likely evolved directly from Cro-Magnons.

Checking Concepts

Choose the word or phrase that best answers the question.

1. What is an example of adaptation?
   A) a fossil
   B) gradualism
   C) camouflage
   D) embryo

2. What method provides the most accurate estimate of a fossil's age?
   A) natural selection
   B) radiometric dating
   C) relative dating
   D) camouflage

3. What do homologous structures, vestigial structures, and fossils provide evidence of?
   A) gradualism
   B) food choice
   C) populations
   D) evolution

4. Which model of evolution shows change over a relatively short period of time?
   A) embryology
   B) adaptation
   C) gradualism
   D) punctuated equilibrium

5. What might a series of helpful variations in a species result in?
   A) adaptation
   B) fossils
   C) embryology
   D) climate change

6. What describes organisms that are adapted to their environment?
   A) homologous
   B) not reproducing
   C) forming fossils
   D) surviving and reproducing

7. What is the study of an organism's early development called?
   A) adaptation
   B) relative dating
   C) natural selection
   D) embryology

8. What animal group(s) have opposable thumbs and binocular vision?
   A) all primates
   B) hominids
   C) humans only
   D) monkeys only

9. Which of the following is a principle of natural selection?
   A) inheritance of acquired traits
   B) Unused traits become smaller.
   C) Organisms produce more offspring than can survive.
   D) the size of an organism

10. A hominid fossil has the same number of bones in its hand as a gorilla. What type of evidence for evolution does this represent?
    A) DNA
    B) embryology
    C) vestigial structures
    D) homologous structures

Thinking Critically

11. How would Lamarck and Darwin have explained the large eyes of an owl?

12. Using an example, explain how a new species of organism could evolve.

13. How is the color-changing ability of chameleons an adaptation?

14. Describe the processes a scientist would use to figure out the age of a fossil.

15. Explain how a species could adapt to its environment. Give an example.

Developing Skills

16. **Predicting** Predict what type of bird the foot pictured below would belong to. Explain your reasoning.

17. Interpreting Data Each letter below represents a chemical found in different species of bacteria. Which species are closely related?

Chemicals Present in Bacteria Species	
Species 1	A, G, T, C, L, E, S, H
Species 2	A, G, T, C, L, D, H
Species 3	A, G, T, C, L, D, P, U, S, R, I, V
Species 4	A, G, T, C, L, D, H

18. Forming Hypotheses Frog eggs are common in ponds in spring. Make a hypothesis as to why ponds are not overpopulated by frogs in summer. Use the concept of natural selection to help you.

19. Comparing and Contrasting Compare and contrast Cro-Magnon humans and modern humans *Homo sapiens sapiens.*

20. Concept Mapping Make an events chain of the events that led Charles Darwin to his theory of evolution by natural selection.

Performance Assessment

21. Collection With permission, collect fossils from your area and identify them. Show your collection to your class.

22. Brochure Assume that you are head of an advertising company hired by Charles Darwin. Develop a brochure to explain Darwin's theory of evolution by natural selection.

TECHNOLOGY

Go to the Glencoe Science Web site at **science.glencoe.com** or use the **Glencoe Science CD-ROM** for additional chapter assessment.

THE PRINCETON REVIEW — Test Practice

A scientist studied a genetic variation in a large family of birds. She made the pedigree below to show how the variations within the family appeared.

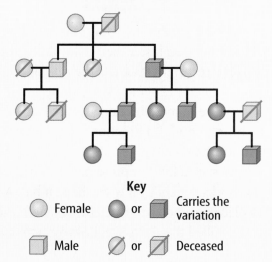

Key

⬭ Female   ⬤ or ⬛ Carries the variation

▭ Male   ⬚ or ⬭ Deceased

Study the pedigree and answer the following questions.

1. Which of the following is most likely the scientist's conclusion from this data?
   A) Female birds of this species die more often than the males.
   B) The variation helps the birds survive and reproduce.
   C) Birds of this species lay one or two eggs.
   D) The genetic variation only helps one of the two sexes.

2. To which offspring is this genetic variation most often passed along?
   F) all offspring
   G) some females and all males
   H) only the father's daughters
   J) males only

Reading Comprehension

Read the passage. Then read each question that follows the passage. Decide which is the best answer to each question.

Enzymes in Humans

A catalyst is a substance that makes a chemical reaction happen faster than it would happen by itself. Interestingly, it affects the rate of the reaction without permanently entering into the reaction. More than 2,000 catalysts are necessary for the human body to function well. These catalysts are called enzymes.

Enzymes are a kind of protein. How an enzyme works depends on what shape it has. A special place on an enzyme attaches to chemicals. This site is called the active site. Enzyme activity can be compared to a lock and a key. Only the correct chemicals, or keys, will fit into the enzyme, or lock. The enzyme brings chemicals together so they can react. This is how enzymes speed up reactions—by making the reactants come together in a more direct way than if they were left to just bump into each other randomly. One enzyme can be used over and over to activate the same reaction. Some enzymes can help reactions go in either direction. In order for an enzyme to work properly, the temperature and pH must be within a certain range. Enough energy and enough reactants also must be present.

The three types of enzymes are metabolic, digestive, and food. Metabolic enzymes catalyze the reactions within cells. They help phosphorus turn into bone, iron attach to red blood cells, and wounds to heal. Digestive enzymes help with the breakdown of foods, allowing nutrients to be absorbed into the bloodstream and used by the body. Food enzymes are supplied through foods that are eaten, and they help with digestion.

Enzymes are essential for many reactions within the human body. Amylase is an enzyme found in saliva. It starts digesting your food before you even swallow!

An enzyme called carbonic anhydrase (kar BAH nihk · an HI drays) helps remove carbon dioxide from your cells. You breathe the carbon dioxide out and replace it with oxygen. Carbonic anhydrase enzyme makes the reaction 107 times faster than if it had to happen on its own! You can see how people depend on enzyme catalysts to maintain health.

Enzymes can be found in all living things. Enzymes also have been used in industry for nearly 100 years. Some of the products that depend on the action of enzymes are leather, alcohol, medications, baking products, detergents, and even fruit juice!

Test-Taking Tip   Make sure that you understand what you are reading as you read a passage. If you are confused by something, stop and read the information again.

---

1. Based on the information in the passage, it can be concluded that _____.
   A) enzymes are found only in humans
   B) amylase is an enzyme that removes oxygen
   C) humans have more than 2,000 enzymes
   D) another word for the locks found in doors is enzyme

2. Enzymes are important to human health because they _____.
   F) are used to help open locks
   G) are used to make leather and fruit juice
   H) speed up the reactions in human bodies
   J) are found in all living things

Reasoning and Skills

Read each question and select the best answer.

1. The object shown here is a(n) _____ because it contains structures surrounded by membranes.
   A) prokaryotic cell
   B) mitochondrion
   C) Golgi body
   D) eukaryotic cell

Test-Taking Tip Think about the way cells are classified into groups.

A)
B)

2. Item A above is different from item B because it _____.
   F) is not organized
   G) does not require energy for its formation
   H) is not composed of cells
   J) does not respond to changes in temperature or pressure

Test-Taking Tip Review the characteristics common to all living things.

3. Cattails and some other plant species can produce new plants without using seeds. What is this process called?
   A) sexual reproduction
   B) variation
   C) asexual reproduction
   D) mutation

Test-Taking Tip Think about the two types of reproduction.

Consider this question carefully before writing your answer on a separate sheet of paper.

4. The virus particle pictured above is not inside a host cell. Give at least one good reason why it could be considered a living organism and one good reason why it could not.

Test-Taking Tip Compare the characteristics of a virus with the characteristics of living organisms.

Student Resources

CONTENTS

Field GUIDE

Feline Traits

Feline Breeds

Siamese

Siamese

This is an ancient breed from Siam, which is now called Thailand. Siamese have long bodies and tails, and their fur is short. They are easy to recognize because they have light-colored bodies and dark ears, masks, tails, and legs. Their eyes are blue.

Devon Rex

Devon Rex

This breed is a natural mutation that first appeared in Devonshire, England, in 1960. Their eyes and batlike ears look huge against their tiny faces. When you stroke a Devon Rex's coat, its fur ripples.

For centuries, humans have lived with cats. They have kept cats in their homes and on their properties. Cats hunt mice and other rodents that eat stored grains and other human foods. Cats also are companions and family pets. Today, the cat is the most popular pet in the United States.

When animals mate, they pass their genetic traits to their offspring. Occasionally, a natural mutation results in a new breed. Sometimes animal scientists try to create new breeds through selective breeding. They study the pedigree, or family history, of several animals of the same species to see what genetic traits they carry. Then they mate the animals that are most likely to pass the desired traits to their offspring. Over time, a new breed can be developed.

The Cat Fancier's Association recognizes 37 breeds of cats. This field guide describes the traits of 14 of these recognized breeds. None of these breeds has come about by recent selective breeding. Some of these breeds have ancient histories, and others have resulted from natural mutations.

Most cats that people adopt today have a mixed ancestry of several breeds. Read about different breeds on the next few pages. Do you know a cat that has one or more of the described traits?

Field Activity

For a week, use this field guide to observe the cats in your neighborhood. What traits do they have? What breeds might be part of their pedigree? Go to the Glencoe Science Web site at **science.glencoe.com** to find more photographs of felines. In your Science Journal, record each cat's name, the traits you noticed, and the breeds that have those traits.

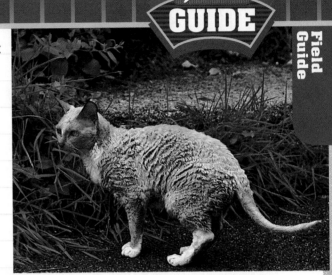

Cornish Rex

Cornish Rex

This natural mutation first appeared in Cornwall, England, in about 1950. Cornish Rex cats remind some people of a skinny breed of dog called a whippet. They have arched backs, small waists, and long legs. Their ears are large, and they have small, egg-shaped heads. Their short, curly fur is soft.

Chartreux

Chartreux [shahr-TROOZ]

This breed dates back at least to the sixteenth century. Their name comes from a type of Spanish wool, but they are considered French cats. Chartreux cats are large and powerful, but they tend to be gentle. They are known for their woolly, bluish coats.

British Shorthair

This breed descends from ancient Roman house cats. They are large, powerful animals with broad chests and round faces. They have short legs and short, thick fur. You might have seen these calm, intelligent cats in TV commercials.

British Shorthair

American Wirehair

This breed is a natural mutation that first appeared in New York in 1966. The feature that makes them special is their unusual coat. Each hair is stiff and crimped, which makes the coat hard. Their whiskers also are wiry.

American Wirehair

Field GUIDE

American Shorthair

This breed came to America with the English Puritans in the 1600s. As the name suggests, they have short fur. They come in many colors, but most are silver with black bands.

Abyssinian (a buh SIH nee un)

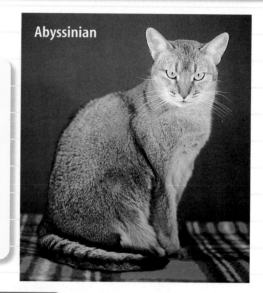

Abyssinian

In the mid-1800s, this breed was brought to England from Ethiopia, which was then called Abyssinia. However, some scientists believe these cats might have originated in Asia. Abyssinians have arched necks, muscular bodies, large ears, and almond-shaped eyes. Their coats can be ruddy, fawn, auburn, or bluish, and they are marked with several dark bands.

Sphynx

Sphynx

The Sphynx is a natural mutation. It first appeared in Canada in 1966. At first glance, these cats appear to be totally bald. In fact, their bodies are covered with a soft, fuzzy, downlike hair. They have short whiskers or none at all, and their skin is often wrinkled.

Selkirk Rex

This breed first appeared as a natural mutation in Wyoming. Selkirk Rexs are large and powerful like the British Shorthair, and they have curly hair and whiskers. Unlike Devon Rex and Cornish Rex, their hair can be long or short. They come in many colors.

Selkirk Rex

Norwegian Forest Cat

These green-eyed cats came to North America with the Viking explorers. In the winter, their hair is thick and a plush mane grows around their necks and chests. The long hair of their inner ears stays with them all year. They come in many colors.

Norwegian Forest Cat

Manx

Manx

This breed first appeared on the Isle of Man. Manx cats are best known as the cats without tails, but some have stubby tails called rises. They have arched backs, round heads, and round bodies. Their hair can be long or short.

Maine Coon

This breed developed in North America and was first recognized in Maine. Maine Coons are large, sturdy cats. Long hair and the tufts of hair in their ears help them tolerate extreme cold. Their coats are shaggy, but they feel silky.

Maine Coon cats

Egyptian Mau

Egyptian Mau

The ancient Egyptians loved to draw this breed, which descends from the African wildcat. Egyptian Maus have green eyes, and their fur can be silver, bronze, black, bluish, or smoke colored. They differ from all other domestic cats because they are the only natural breed with a spotted coat.

As you study science, you will make many observations and conduct investigations and experiments. You will also research information that is available from many sources. These activities will involve organizing and recording data. The quality of the data you collect and the way you organize it will determine how well others can understand and use it. In **Figure 1,** the student is obtaining and recording information using a microscope.

Putting your observations in writing is an important way of communicating to others the information you have found and the results of your investigations and experiments.

Researching Information

Scientists work to build on and add to human knowledge of the world. Before moving in a new direction, it is important to gather the information that already is known about a subject. You will look for such information in various reference sources. Follow these steps to research information on a scientific subject:

Step 1 Determine exactly what you need to know about the subject. For instance, you might want to find out what happened to local plant life when Mount St. Helens erupted in 1980.

Step 2 Make a list of questions, such as: When did the eruption begin? How long did it last? How large was the area in which plant life was affected?

Step 3 Use multiple sources such as textbooks, encyclopedias, government documents, professional journals, science magazines, and the Internet.

Step 4 List where you found the sources. Make sure the sources you use are reliable and the most current available.

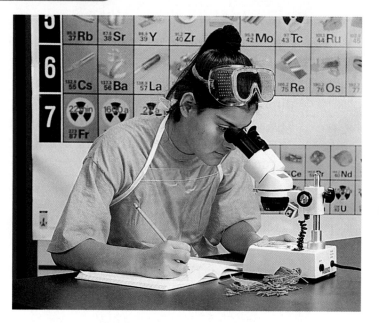

Figure 1
Making an observation is one way to gather information directly.

Evaluating Print and Nonprint Sources

Not all sources of information are reliable. Evaluate the sources you use for information, and use only those you know to be dependable. For example, suppose you want information about the digestion of fats and proteins. You might find two Websites on digestion. One Web site contains "Fat Zapping Tips" written by a company that sells expensive, high-protein supplements to help your body eliminate excess fat. The other is a Web page on "Digestion and Metabolism" written by a well-respected medical school. You would choose the second Web site as the more reliable source of information.

In science, information can change rapidly. Always consult the most current sources. A 1985 source about the human genome would not reflect the most recent research and findings.

Interpreting Scientific Illustrations

As you research a science topic, you will see drawings, diagrams, and photographs. Illustrations help you understand what you read. Some illustrations are included to help you understand an idea that you can't see easily by yourself. For instance, you can't see the bones of a blue whale, but you can look at a diagram of a whale skeleton as labeled in **Figure 2** that helps you understand them. Visualizing a drawing helps many people remember details more easily. Illustrations also provide examples that clarify difficult concepts or give additional information about the topic you are studying.

Most illustrations have a label or a caption. A label or caption identifies the illustration or provides additional information to better explain it. Can you find the caption or labels in **Figure 2?**

Figure 2
A labeled diagram of the skeletal structure of a blue whale.

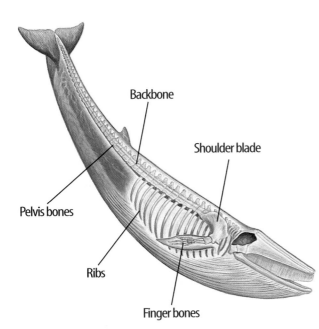

Backbone

Shoulder blade

Pelvis bones

Ribs

Finger bones

Concept Mapping

If you were taking a car trip, you might take some sort of road map. By using a map, you begin to learn where you are in relation to other places on the map.

A concept map is similar to a road map, but a concept map shows relationships among ideas (or concepts) rather than places. It is a diagram that visually shows how concepts are related. Because a concept map shows relationships among ideas, it can make the meanings of ideas and terms clear and help you understand what you are studying.

Overall, concept maps are useful for breaking large concepts down into smaller parts, making learning easier.

Venn Diagram

Although it is not a concept map, a Venn diagram illustrates how two subjects compare and contrast. In other words, you can see the characteristics that the subjects have in common and those that they do not.

The Venn diagram in **Figure 3** shows the relationship between two categories of organisms, plants and animals. Both share some basic characteristics as living organisms. However, there are differences in the ways they carry out various life processes, such as obtaining nourishment, that distinguish one from the other.

Figure 3
A Venn diagram shows how objects or concepts are alike and how they are different.

Plants
(make their own food, stationary)

Animals
(eat plants or other animals, move from place to place)

Alive
(reproduce, grow, and develop)

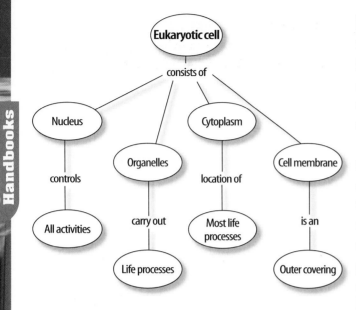

Figure 4
A network tree shows how concepts or objects are related.

Network Tree Look at the concept map in **Figure 4,** that shows details about a eukaryotic cell. This is called a network tree concept map. Notice how some words are in ovals while others are written across connecting lines. The words inside the ovals are science terms or concepts. The words written on the connecting lines describe the relationships between the concepts.

When constructing a network tree, write the topic on a note card or piece of paper. Write the major concepts related to that topic on separate note cards or pieces of paper. Then arrange them in order from general to specific. Branch the related concepts from the major concept and describe the relationships on the connecting lines. Continue branching to more specific concepts. Write the relationships between the concepts on the connecting lines until all concepts are mapped. Then examine the concept map for relationships that cross branches, and add them to the concept map.

Events Chain An events chain is another type of concept map. It models the order of items or their sequence. In science, an events chain can be used to describe a sequence of events, the steps in a procedure, or the stages of a process.

When making an events chain, first find the one event that starts the chain. This event is called the *initiating event.* Then, find the next event in the chain and continue until you reach an outcome. Suppose you are asked to describe the main stages in the growth of a plant from a seed. You might draw an events chain such as the one in **Figure 5.** Notice that connecting words are not necessary in an events chain.

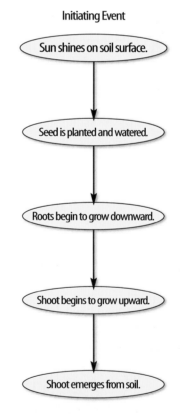

Figure 5
Events chains show the order of steps in a process or event.

Cycle Map A cycle concept map is a specific type of events chain map. In a cycle concept map, the series of events does not produce a final outcome. Instead, the last event in the chain relates back to the beginning event.

You first decide what event will be used as the beginning event. Once that is decided, you list events in order that occur after it. Words are written between events that describe what happens from one event to the next. The last event in a cycle concept map relates back to the beginning event. The number of events in a cycle concept varies, but is usually three or more. Look at the cycle map, as shown in **Figure 6.**

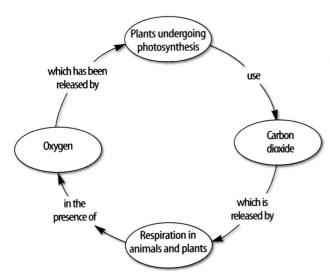

Figure 6
A cycle map shows events that occur in a cycle.

Spider Map A type of concept map that you can use for brainstorming is the spider map. When you have a central idea, you might find you have a jumble of ideas that relate to it but may not clearly relate to each other. The circulatory system spider map in **Figure 7** shows that if you write these ideas outside the main concept, then you can begin to separate and group unrelated terms so they become more useful.

Figure 7
A spider map allows you to list ideas that relate to a central topic but not necessarily to one another.

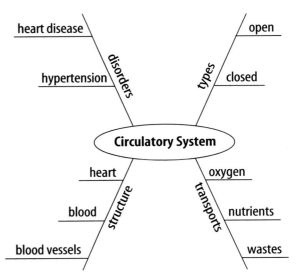

Writing a Paper

You will write papers often when researching science topics or reporting the results of investigations or experiments. Scientists frequently write papers to share their data and conclusions with other scientists and the public. When writing a paper, use these steps.

Step 1 Assemble your data by using graphs, tables, or a concept map. Create an outline.

Step 2 Start with an introduction that contains a clear statement of purpose and what you intend to discuss or prove.

Step 3 Organize the body into paragraphs. Each paragraph should start with a topic sentence, and the remaining sentences in that paragraph should support your point.

Step 4 Position data to help support your points.

Step 5 Summarize the main points and finish with a conclusion statement.

Step 6 Use tables, graphs, charts, and illustrations whenever possible.

You might say the work of a scientist is to solve problems. When you decide to find out why one corner of your yard is always soggy, you are problem solving, too. You might observe the corner is lower than the surrounding area and has less vegetation growing in it. You might decide to see if planting some grass will keep the corner drier.

Scientists use orderly approaches to solve problems. The methods scientists use include identifying a question, making observations, forming a hypothesis, testing a hypothesis, analyzing results, and drawing conclusions.

Scientific investigations involve careful observation under controlled conditions. Such observation of an object or a process can suggest new and interesting questions about it. These questions sometimes lead to the formation of a hypothesis. Scientific investigations are designed to test a hypothesis.

Identifying a Question

The first step in a scientific investigation or experiment is to identify a question to be answered or a problem to be solved. You might be interested in knowing why an animal like the one in **Figure 8** look the way they do.

Figure 8
When you see a bird, you might ask yourself, "How does the shape of this bird's beak help it feed?"

Forming Hypotheses

Hypotheses are based on observations that have been made. A hypothesis is a possible explanation based on previous knowledge and observations.

Perhaps a scientist has observed that bean plants grow larger if they are fertilized than if not. Based on these observations, the scientist can make a statement that he or she can test. The statement is a hypothesis. The hypothesis could be: *Fertilizer makes bean plants grow larger.* A hypothesis has to be something you can test by using an investigation. A testable hypothesis is a valid hypothesis.

Predicting

When you apply a hypothesis, or general explanation, to a specific situation, you predict something about that situation. First, you must identify which hypothesis fits the situation you are considering. People use predictions to make everyday decisions. Based on previous observations and experiences, you might form a prediction that if fertilizer makes bean plants grow larger, then fertilized plants will yield more beans than plants not fertilized. Someone could use this prediction to plan to grow fewer plants.

Testing a Hypothesis

To test a hypothesis, you need a procedure. A procedure is the plan you follow in your experiment. A procedure tells you what materials to use, as well as how and in what order to use them. When you follow a procedure, data are generated that support or do not support the original hypothesis statement.

For example, suppose you notice that your guppies don't seem as active as usual when your aquarium heater is not working. You wonder how water temperature affects guppy activity level. You decide to test the hypothesis, "If water temperature increases, then guppy activity should increase." Then you write the procedure shown in **Figure 9** for your experiment and generate the data presented in the table below.

Procedure

1. Fill five identical glass containers with equal amounts of aquarium water.
2. Measure and record the temperature of the water in the first container.
3. Heat and cool the other containers so that two have higher and two have lower water temperatures.
4. Place a guppy in each container; count and record the number of movements each guppy makes in 5 minutes.

Figure 9
A procedure tells you what to do step by step.

Number of Guppy Movements		
Container	Temperature (°C)	Movements
1	38	56
2	40	61
3	42	70
4	36	46
5	34	42

Are all investigations alike? Keep in mind as you perform investigations in science that a hypothesis can be tested in many ways. Not every investigation makes use of all the ways that are described on these pages, and not all hypotheses are tested by investigations. Scientists encounter many variations in the methods that are used when they perform experiments. The skills in this handbook are here for you to use and practice.

Identifying and Manipulating Variables and Controls

In any experiment, it is important to keep everything the same except for the item you are testing. The one factor you change is called the independent variable. The factor that changes as a result of the independent variable is called the dependent variable. Always make sure you have only one independent variable. If you allow more than one, you will not know what causes the changes you observe in the dependent variable. Many experiments also have controls—individual instances or experimental subjects for which the independent variable is not changed. You can then compare the test results to the control results.

For example, in the guppy experiment, you made everything the same except the temperature of the water. The glass containers were identical. The volume of aquarium water in each container and beginning water temperature were the same. Each guppy was like the others, as much as possible. In this way, you could be sure that any difference in the number of guppy movements was caused by the temperature change—the independent variable. The activity level of the guppy was measured as the number of guppy movements—the dependent variable. The guppy in the container in which the water temperature was not changed was the control.

Collecting Data

Whether you are carrying out an investigation or a short observational experiment, you will collect data, or information. Scientists collect data accurately as numbers and descriptions and organize it in specific ways.

Observing Scientists observe items and events, then record what they see. When they use only words to describe an observation, it is called qualitative data. For example, a scientist might describe the color of a bird or the shape of a bird's beak as seen through binoculars. Scientists' observations also can describe how much there is of something. These observations use numbers, as well as words, in the description and are called quantitative data. For example, if a particular dog is described as being "furry, yellow, and short-haired," the data are clearly qualitative. Quantitative data for this dog might include "a mass of 14 kg, a height of 46 cm, and an age of 150 days." Quantitative data often are organized into tables. Then, from information in the table, a graph can be drawn. Graphs can reveal relationships that exist in experimental data.

When you make observations in science, you should examine the entire object or situation first, then look carefully for details. If you're looking at a plant, for instance, check general characteristics such as size and overall structure before using a hand lens to examine the leaves and other smaller structures such as flowers or fruits. Remember to record accurately everything you see.

Scientists try to make careful and accurate observations. When possible, they use instruments such as microscopes, metric rulers, graduated cylinders, thermometers, and balances. Measurements provide numerical data that can be repeated and checked.

Sampling When working with large numbers of objects or a large population, scientists usually cannot observe or study every one of them. Instead, they use a sample or a portion of the total number. To *sample* is to take a small, representative portion of the objects or organisms of a population for research. By making careful observations or manipulating variables within a portion of a group, information is discovered and conclusions are drawn that might apply to the whole population.

Estimating Scientific work also involves estimating. To *estimate* is to make a judgment about the size or the number of something without measuring or counting every object or member of a population. Scientists first count the number of objects in a small sample. Looking through a microscope lens, for example, a scientist can count the number of bacterial colonies in the 1-cm^2 frame shown in **Figure 10.** Then the scientist can multiply that number by the number of cm^2 in the petri dish to get an estimate of the total number of bacterial colonies present.

Figure 10
To estimate the total number of bacterial colonies that are present on a petri dish, count the number of bacterial colonies within a 1-cm^2 frame and multiply that number by the number of frames on the dish.

Measuring in SI

The metric system of measurement was developed in 1795. A modern form of the metric system, called the International System, or SI, was adopted in 1960. SI provides standard measurements that all scientists around the world can understand.

The metric system is convenient because unit sizes vary by multiples of 10. When changing from smaller units to larger units, divide by a multiple of 10. When changing from larger units to smaller, multiply by a multiple of 10. To convert millimeters to centimeters, divide the millimeters by 10. To convert 30 mm to centimeters, divide 30 by 10 (30 mm equal 3 cm).

Prefixes are used to name units. Look at the table below for some common metric prefixes and their meanings. Do you see how the prefix *kilo-* attached to the unit *gram* is *kilogram*, or 1,000 g?

Metric Prefixes

Prefix	Symbol	Meaning	
kilo-	k	1,000	thousand
hecto-	h	100	hundred
deka-	da	10	ten
deci-	d	0.1	tenth
centi-	c	0.01	hundredth
milli-	m	0.001	thousandth

Now look at the metric ruler shown in **Figure 11.** The centimeter lines are the long, numbered lines, and the shorter lines are millimeter lines.

When using a metric ruler, line up the 0-cm mark with the end of the object being measured, and read the number of the unit where the object ends, in this instance it would be 4.5 cm.

Figure 11
This metric ruler shows centimeters and millimeter divisions.

Liquid Volume In some science activities, you will measure liquids. The unit that is used to measure liquids is the liter. A liter has the volume of 1,000 cm³. The prefix *milli-* means "thousandth (0.001)." A milliliter is one thousandth of 1 L and 1 L has the volume of 1,000 mL. One milliliter of liquid completely fills a cube measuring 1 cm on each side. Therefore, 1 mL equals 1 cm³.

You will use beakers and graduated cylinders to measure liquid volume. A graduated cylinder, as illustrated in **Figure 12,** is marked from bottom to top in milliliters. This graduated cylinder contains 79 mL of a liquid.

Figure 12
Graduated cylinders measure liquid volume.

Mass Scientists measure mass in grams. You might use a beam balance similar to the one shown in **Figure 13.** The balance has a pan on one side and a set of beams on the other side. Each beam has a rider that slides on the beam.

Before you find the mass of an object, slide all the riders back to the zero point. Check the pointer on the right to make sure it swings an equal distance above and below the zero point. If the swing is unequal, find and turn the adjusting screw until you have an equal swing.

Place an object on the pan. Slide the largest rider along its beam until the pointer drops below zero. Then move it back one notch. Repeat the process on each beam until the pointer swings an equal distance above and below the zero point. Sum the masses on each beam to find the mass of the object. Move all riders back to zero when finished.

Figure 13
A triple beam balance is used to determine the mass of an object.

You should never place a hot object on the pan or pour chemicals directly onto the pan. Instead, find the mass of a clean container. Remove the container from the pan, then place the chemicals in the container. Find the mass of the container with the chemicals in it. To find the mass of the chemicals, subtract the mass of the empty container from the mass of the filled container.

Making and Using Tables

Browse through your textbook and you will see tables in the text and in the activities. In a table, data, or information, are arranged so that they are easier to understand. Activity tables help organize the data you collect during an activity so results can be interpreted.

Making Tables To make a table, list the items to be compared in the first column and the characteristics to be compared in the first row. The title should clearly indicate the content of the table, and the column or row heads should tell the reader what information is found in there. The table below lists materials collected for recycling on three weekly pick-up days. The inclusion of kilograms in parentheses also identifies for the reader that the figures are mass units.

Recyclable Materials Collected During Week			
Day of Week	Paper (kg)	Aluminum (kg)	Glass (kg)
Monday	5.0	4.0	12.0
Wednesday	4.0	1.0	10.0
Friday	2.5	2.0	10.0

Using Tables How much paper, in kilograms, is being recycled on Wednesday? Locate the column labeled "Paper (kg)" and the row "Wednesday." The information in the box where the column and row intersect is the answer. Did you answer "4.0"? How much aluminum, in kilograms, is being recycled on Friday? If you answered "2.0," you understand how to read the table. How much glass is collected for recycling each week? Locate the column labeled "Glass (kg)" and add the figures for all three rows. If you answered "32.0," then you know how to locate and use the data provided in the table.

Recording Data

To be useful, the data you collect must be recorded carefully. Accuracy is key. A well-thought-out experiment includes a way to record procedures, observations, and results accurately. Data tables are one way to organize and record results. Set up the tables you will need ahead of time so you can record the data right away.

Record information properly and neatly. Never put unidentified data on scraps of paper. Instead, data should be written in a notebook like the one in **Figure 14.** Write in pencil so information isn't lost if your data gets wet. At each point in the experiment, record your data and label it. That way, your information will be accurate and you will not have to determine what the figures mean when you look at your notes later.

Figure 14
Record data neatly and clearly so it is easy to understand.

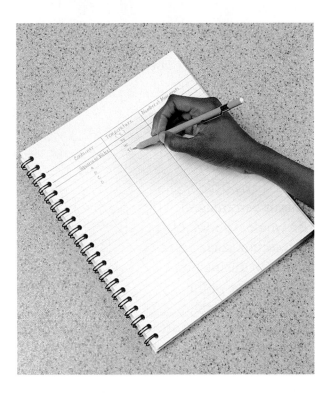

Recording Observations

It is important to record observations accurately and completely. That is why you always should record observations in your notes immediately as you make them. It is easy to miss details or make mistakes when recording results from memory. Do not include your personal thoughts when you record your data. Record only what you observe to eliminate bias. For example, when you record that a plant grew 12 cm in one day, you would note that this was the largest daily growth for the week. However, you would not refer to the data as "the best growth spurt of the week."

Making Models

You can organize the observations and other data you collect and record in many ways. Making models is one way to help you better understand the parts of a structure you have been observing or the way a process for which you have been taking various measurements works.

Models often show things that are very large or small or otherwise would be difficult to see and understand. You can study blood vessels and know that they are hollow tubes. The size and proportional differences among arteries, veins, and capillaries can be explained in words. However, you can better visualize the relative sizes and proportions of blood vessels by making models of them. Gluing different kinds of pasta to thick paper so the openings can be seen can help you see how the differences in size, wall thickness, and shape among types of blood vessels affect their functions.

Other models can be devised on a computer. Some models, such as disease control models used by doctors to predict the spread of the flu, are mathematical and are represented by equations.

Making and Using Graphs

After scientists organize data in tables, they might display the data in a graph that shows the relationship of one variable to another. A graph makes interpretation and analysis of data easier. Three types of graphs are the line graph, the bar graph, and the circle graph.

Line Graphs A line graph like in **Figure 15** is used to show the relationship between two variables. The variables being compared go on two axes of the graph. For data from an experiment, the independent variable always goes on the horizontal axis, called the *x*-axis. The dependent variable always goes on the vertical axis, called the *y*-axis. After drawing your axes, label each with a scale. Next, plot the data points.

A data point is the intersection of the recorded value of the dependent variable for each tested value of the independent variable. After all the points are plotted, connect them.

Bar Graphs Bar graphs compare data that do not change continuously. Vertical bars show the relationships among data.

To make a bar graph, set up the *y*-axis as you did for the line graph. Draw vertical bars of equal size from the *x*-axis up to the point on the *y*-axis that represents value of *x*.

Figure 16
The number of wing vibrations per second for different insects can be shown as a bar graph or circle graph.

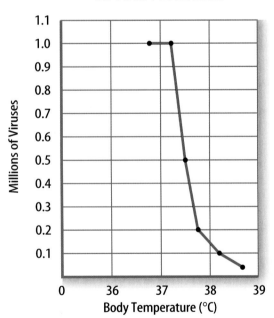

Figure 15
This line graph shows the relationship between body temperature and the millions of infecting viruses present in a human body.

Circle Graphs A circle graph uses a circle divided into sections to display data as parts (fractions or percentages) of a whole. The size of each section corresponds to the fraction or percentage of the data that the section represents. So, the entire circle represents 100 percent, one-half represents 50 percent, one-fifth represents 20 percent, and so on.

Analyzing Results

To determine the meaning of your observations and investigation results, you will need to look for patterns in the data. You can organize your information in several of the ways that are discussed in this handbook. Then you must think critically to determine what the data mean. Scientists use several approaches when they analyze the data they have collected and recorded. Each approach is useful for identifying specific patterns in the data.

Forming Operational Definitions

An operational definition defines an object by showing how it functions, works, or behaves. Such definitions are written in terms of how an object works or how it can be used; that is, they describe its job or purpose.

For example, a ruler can be defined as a tool that measures the length of an object (how it can be used). A ruler also can be defined as something that contains a series of marks that can be used as a standard when measuring (how it works).

Classifying

Classifying is the process of sorting objects or events into groups based on common features. When classifying, first observe the objects or events to be classified. Then select one feature that is shared by some members in the group but not by all. Place those members that share that feature into a subgroup. You can classify members into smaller and smaller subgroups based on characteristics.

How might you classify a group of animals? You might first classify them by putting all of the dogs, cats, lizards, snakes, and birds into separate groups. Within each group, you could then look for another common feature by which to further classify members of the group, such as size or color.

Remember that when you classify, you are grouping objects or events for a purpose. For example, classifying animals can be the first step in identifying them. You might know that a cardinal is a red bird. To find it in a large group of animals, you might start with the classification scheme mentioned above. You'll locate a cardinal within the red grouping of the birds that you separate from the rest of the animals. A male ruby-throated hummingbird could be located within the birds by its tiny size and the bright red color of its throat. Keep your purpose in mind as you select the features to form groups and subgroups.

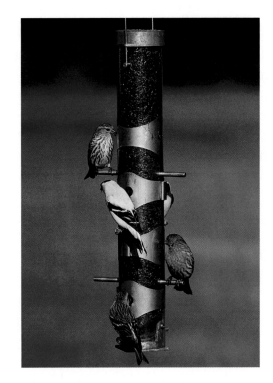

Figure 17
Color is one of many characteristics that are used to classify animals.

Science Skill Handbook

Comparing and Contrasting

Observations can be analyzed by noting the similarities and differences between two or more objects or events that you observe. When you look at objects or events to see how they are similar, you are comparing them. Contrasting is looking for differences in objects or events. The table below compares and contrasts the nutritional value of two cereals.

Nutritional Values		
	Cereal A	Cereal B
Calories	220	160
Fat	10 g	10 g
Protein	2.5 g	2.6 g
Carbohydrate	30 g	15 g

Recognizing Cause and Effect

Have you ever gotten a cold and then suggested that you probably caught it from a classmate who had one recently? If so, you have observed an effect and inferred a cause. The event is the effect, and the reason for the event is the cause.

When scientists are unsure of the cause of a certain event, they design controlled experiments to determine what caused it.

Interpreting Data

The word *interpret* means "to explain the meaning of something." Look at the problem originally being explored in an experiment and figure out what the data show. Identify the control group and the test group so you can see whether or not changes in the independent variable have had an effect. Look for differences in the dependent variable between the control and test groups.

These differences you observe can be qualitative or quantitative. You would be able to describe a qualitative difference using only words, whereas you would measure a quantitative difference and describe it using numbers. If there are qualitative or quantitative differences, the independent variable that is being tested could have had an effect. If no qualitative or quantitative differences are found between the control and test groups, the variable that is being tested apparently had no effect.

For example, suppose that three pepper plants are placed in a garden and two of the plants are fertilized, but the third is left to grow without fertilizer. Suppose you are then asked to describe any differences in the plants after two weeks. A qualitative difference might be the appearance of brighter green leaves on fertilized plants but not on the unfertilized plant. A quantitative difference might be a difference in the height of the plants or the number of flowers on them.

Inferring Scientists often make inferences based on their observations. An inference is an attempt to explain, or interpret, observations or to indicate what caused what you observed. An inference is a type of conclusion.

When making an inference, be certain to use accurate data and accurately described observations. Analyze all of the data that you've collected. Then, based on everything you know, explain or interpret what you've observed.

Drawing Conclusions

When scientists have analyzed the data they collected, they proceed to draw conclusions about what the data mean. These conclusions are sometimes stated using words similar to those found in the hypothesis formed earlier in the process.

Conclusions To analyze your data, you must review all of the observations and measurements that you made and recorded. Recheck all data for accuracy. After your data are rechecked and organized, you are almost ready to draw a conclusion such as "Plants need sunlight in order to grow."

Before you can draw a conclusion, however, you must determine whether the data allow you to come to a conclusion that supports a hypothesis. Sometimes that will be the case, other times it will not.

If your data do not support a hypothesis, it does not mean that the hypothesis is wrong. It means only that the results of the investigation did not support the hypothesis. Maybe the experiment needs to be redesigned, but very likely, some of the initial observations on which the hypothesis was based were incomplete or biased. Perhaps more observation or research is needed to refine the hypothesis.

Avoiding Bias Sometimes drawing a conclusion involves making judgments. When you make a judgment, you form an opinion about what your data mean. It is important to be honest and to avoid reaching a conclusion if there were no supporting evidence for it or if it were based on a small sample. It also is important not to allow any expectations of results to bias your judgments. If possible, it is a good idea to collect additional data. Scientists do this all the time.

For example, animal behaviorist Katharine Payne made an important observation about elephant communication. While visiting a zoo, Payne felt the air vibrating around her. At the same time, she also noticed that the skin on an elephant's forehead was fluttering. She suspected that the elephants were generating the vibrations and that they might be using the low-frequency sounds to communicate.

Payne conducted an experiment to record these sounds and simultaneously observe the behavior of the elephants in the zoo. She later conducted a similar experiment in Namibia in southwest Africa, where elephant herds roam. The additional data she collected supported the judgment Payne had made, which was that these low-frequency sounds were a form of communication between elephants.

Evaluating Others' Data and Conclusions

Sometimes scientists have to use data that they did not collect themselves, or they have to rely on observations and conclusions drawn by other researchers. In cases such as these, the data must be evaluated carefully.

How were the data obtained? How was the investigation done? Has it been duplicated by other researchers? Did they come up with the same results? Look at the conclusion, as well. Would you reach the same conclusion from these results? Only when you have confidence in the data of others can you believe it is true and feel comfortable using it.

Communicating

The communication of ideas is an important part of the work of scientists. A discovery that is not reported will not advance the scientific community's understanding or knowledge. Communication among scientists also is important as a way of improving their investigations.

Scientists communicate in many ways, from writing articles in journals and magazines that explain their investigations and experiments, to announcing important discoveries on television and radio, to sharing ideas with colleagues on the Internet or presenting them as lectures.

Computer Skills

People who study science rely on computers to record and store data and to analyze results from investigations. Whether you work in a laboratory or just need to write a lab report with tables, good computer skills are a necessity.

Using a Word Processor

Suppose your teacher has assigned a written report. After you've completed your research and decided how you want to write the information, you need to put all that information on paper. The easiest way to do this is with a word processing application on a computer.

A computer application that allows you to type your information, change it as many times as you need to, and then print it out so that it looks neat and clean is called a word processing application. You also can use this type of application to create tables and columns, add bullets or cartoon art to your page, include page numbers, and even check your spelling.

Helpful Hints

■ If you aren't sure how to do something using your word processing program, look in the help menu. You will find a list of topics there to click on for help. After you locate the help topic you need, just follow the step-by-step instructions you see on your screen.

■ Just because you've spell checked your report doesn't mean that the spelling is perfect. The spell check feature can't catch misspelled words that look like other words. If you've accidentally typed *wind* instead of *wing*, the spell checker won't know the difference. Always reread your report to make sure you didn't miss any mistakes.

Figure 18
You can use computer programs to make graphs and tables.

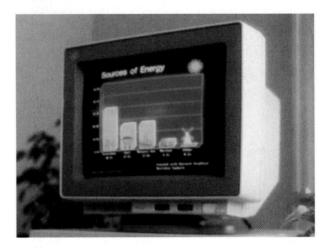

Using a Database

Imagine you're in the middle of a research project busily gathering facts and information. You soon realize that it's becoming more difficult to organize and keep track of all the information. The tool to use to solve information overload is a database. Just as a file cabinet organizes paper records, a database organizes computer records. However, a database is more powerful than a simple file cabinet because at the click of a mouse, the contents can be reshuffled and reorganized. At computer-quick speeds, databases can sort information by any characteristics and filter data into multiple categories.

Helpful Hints

■ Before setting up a database, take some time to learn the features of your database software by practicing with established database software.

■ Periodically save your database as you enter data. That way, if something happens such as your computer malfunctions or the power goes off, you won't lose all of your work.

Doing a Database Search

When searching for information in a database, use the following search strategies to get the best results. These are the same search methods used for searching Internet databases.

■ Place the word *and* between two words in your search if you want the database to look for any entries that have both the words. For example, "fox *and* mink" would give you information that mentions both fox and mink.

■ Place the word *or* between two words if you want the database to show entries that have at least one of the words. For example "fox *or* mink" would show you information that mentions either fox or mink.

■ Place the word *not* between two words if you want the database to look for entries that have the first word but do not have the second word. For example, "canine *not* fox" would show you information that mentions the term canine but does not mention the fox.

In summary, databases can be used to store large amounts of information about a particular subject. Databases allow biologists, Earth scientists, and physical scientists to search for information quickly and accurately.

Using an Electronic Spreadsheet

Your science fair experiment has produced lots of numbers. How do you keep track of all the data, and how can you easily work out all the calculations needed? You can use a computer program called a spreadsheet to record data that involve numbers. A spreadsheet is an electronic mathematical worksheet.

Type in your data in rows and columns, just as in a data table on a sheet of paper. A spreadsheet uses simple math to do data calculations. For example, you could add, subtract, divide, or multiply any of the values in the spreadsheet by another number. You also could set up a series of math steps you want to apply to the data. If you want to add 12 to all the numbers and then multiply all the numbers by 10, the computer does all the calculations for you in the spreadsheet. Below is an example of a spreadsheet that records data from an experiment with mice in a maze.

Helpful Hints

■ Before you set up the spreadsheet, identify how you want to organize the data. Include any formulas you will need to use.

■ Make sure you have entered the correct data into the correct rows and columns.

■ You also can display your results in a graph. Pick the style of graph that best represents the data with which you are working.

Figure 19
A spreadsheet allows you to display large amounts of data and do calculations automatically.

	A	B	C	D	E
1	Test Runs	Time	Distance	Number of turns	
2	Mouse 1	15 seconds	1 meter	3	
3	Mouse 2	12 seconds	1 meter	2	
4	Mouse 3	20 seconds	1 meter	5	

Using a Computerized Card Catalog

When you have a report or paper to research, you probably go to the library. To find the information you need in the library, you might have to use a computerized card catalog. This type of card catalog allows you to search for information by subject, by title, or by author. The computer then will display all the holdings the library has on the subject, title, or author requested.

A library's holdings can include books, magazines, databases, videos, and audio materials. When you have chosen something from this list, the computer will show whether an item is available and where in the library to find it.

Helpful Hints

- Remember that you can use the computer to search by subject, author, or title. If you know a book's author but not the title, you can search for all the books the library has by that author.
- When searching by subject, it's often most helpful to narrow your search by using specific search terms, such as *and, or,* and *not.* If you don't find enough sources, you can broaden your search.
- Pay attention to the type of materials found in your search. If you need a book, you can eliminate any videos or other resources that come up in your search.
- Knowing how your library is arranged can save you a lot of time. The librarian will show you where certain types of materials are kept and how to find specific holdings.

Using Graphics Software

Are you having trouble finding that exact piece of art you're looking for? Do you have a picture in your mind of what you want but can't seem to find the right graphic to represent your ideas? To solve these problems, you can use graphics software. Graphics software allows you to create and change images and diagrams in almost unlimited ways. Typical uses for graphics software include arranging clip art, changing scanned images, and constructing pictures from scratch. Most graphics software applications work in similar ways. They use the same basic tools and functions. Once you master one graphics application, you can use any other graphics application relatively easily.

Figure 20
Graphics software can use your data to draw bar graphs.

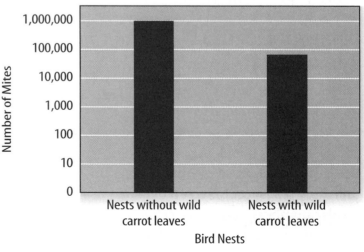

Figure 21
Graphics software can use your data to draw circle graphs.

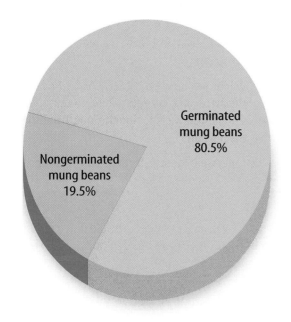

Germinated mung beans
80.5%

Nongerminated mung beans
19.5%

First, determine what important points you want to make in your presentation. Then, write an outline of what materials and types of media would best illustrate those points. Maybe you could start with an outline on an overhead projector, then show a video, followed by something from the Internet or a slide show accompanied by music or recorded voices. You might choose to use a presentation builder computer application that can combine all these elements into one presentation. Make sure the presentation is well constructed to make the most impact on the audience.

Figure 22
Multimedia presentations use many types of print and electronic materials.

Helpful Hints
- As with any method of drawing, the more you practice using the graphics software, the better your results will be.
- Start by using the software to manipulate existing drawings. Once you master this, making your own illustrations will be easier.
- Clip art is available on CD-ROMs and the Internet. With these resources, finding a piece of clip art to suit your purposes is simple.
- As you work on a drawing, save it often.

Developing Multimedia Presentations

It's your turn—you have to present your science report to the entire class. How do you do it? You can use many different sources of information to get the class excited about your presentation. Posters, videos, photographs, sound, computers, and the Internet can help show your ideas.

Helpful Hints
- Carefully consider what media will best communicate the point you are trying to make.
- Make sure you know how to use any equipment you will be using in your presentation.
- Practice the presentation several times.
- If possible, set up all of the equipment ahead of time. Make sure everything is working correctly.

Math Skill Handbook

Use this Math Skill Handbook to help solve problems you are given in this text. You might find it useful to review topics in this Math Skill Handbook first.

Converting Units

In science, quantities such as length, mass, and time sometimes are measured using different units. Suppose you want to know how many miles are in 12.7 km?

Conversion factors are used to change from one unit of measure to another. A conversion factor is a ratio that is equal to one. For example, there are 1,000 mL in 1 L, so 1,000 mL equals 1 L, or:

$$1,000 \text{ mL} = 1 \text{ L}$$

If both sides are divided by 1 L, this equation becomes:

$$\frac{1,000 \text{ mL}}{1 \text{ L}} = 1$$

The **ratio** on the left side of this equation is equal to one and is a conversion factor. You can make another conversion factor by dividing both sides of the top equation by 1,000 mL:

$$1 = \frac{1 \text{ L}}{1,000 \text{ mL}}$$

To **convert units,** you multiply by the appropriate conversion factor. For example, how many milliliters are in 1.255 L? To convert 1.255 L to milliliters, multiply 1.255 L by a conversion factor.

Use the **conversion factor** with new units (mL) in the numerator and the old units (L) in the denominator.

$$1.255 \text{ L} \times \frac{1,000 \text{ mL}}{1 \text{ L}} = 1,255 \text{ mL}$$

The unit L divides in this equation, just as if it were a number.

Example 1 There are 2.54 cm in 1 inch. If a meterstick has a length of 100 cm, how long is the meterstick in inches?

Step 1 Decide which conversion factor to use. You know the length of the meterstick in centimeters, so centimeters are the old units. You want to find the length in inches, so inch is the new unit.

Step 2 Form the conversion factor. Start with the relationship between the old and new units.

$$2.54 \text{ cm} = 1 \text{ inch}$$

Step 3 Form the conversion factor with the old unit (centimeter) on the bottom by dividing both sides by 2.54 cm.

$$1 = \frac{2.54 \text{ cm}}{2.54 \text{ cm}} = \frac{1 \text{ inch}}{2.54 \text{ cm}}$$

Step 4 Multiply the old measurement by the conversion factor.

$$100 \text{ cm} \times \frac{1 \text{ inch}}{2.54 \text{ cm}} = 39.37 \text{ inches}$$

The meter stick is 39.37 inches long.

Example 2 There are 365 days in one year. If a person is 14 years old, what is his or her age in days? (Ignore leap years)

Step 1 Decide which conversion factor to use. You want to convert years to days.

Step 2 Form the conversion factor. Start with the relation between the old and new units.

$$1 \text{ year} = 365 \text{ days}$$

Step 3 Form the conversion factor with the old unit (year) on the bottom by dividing both sides by 1 year.

$$1 = \frac{1 \text{ year}}{1 \text{ year}} = \frac{365 \text{ days}}{1 \text{ year}}$$

Step 4 Multiply the old measurement by the conversion factor:

$$14 \text{ years} \times \frac{365 \text{ days}}{1 \text{ year}} = 5,110 \text{ days}$$

The person's age is 5,110 days.

Practice Problem A cat has a mass of 2.31 kg. If there are 1,000 g in 1 kg, what is the mass of the cat in grams?

Using Fractions

A **fraction** is a number that compares a part to the whole. For example, in the fraction $\frac{2}{3}$, the 2 represents the part and the 3 represents the whole. In the fraction $\frac{2}{3}$, the top number, 2, is called the numerator. The bottom number, 3, is called the denominator.

Sometimes fractions are not written in their simplest form. To determine a fraction's **simplest form,** you must find the greatest common factor (GCF) of the numerator and denominator. The greatest common factor is the largest common factor of all the factors the two numbers have in common.

For example, because the number 3 divides into 12 and 30 evenly, it is a common factor of 12 and 30. However, because the number 6 is the largest number that evenly divides into 12 and 30, it is the **greatest common factor.**

After you find the greatest common factor, you can write a fraction in its simplest form. Divide both the numerator and the denominator by the greatest common factor. The number that results is the fraction in its **simplest form.**

Example Twelve of the 20 corn plants in a field are over 1.5 m tall. What fraction of the corn plants in the field are over 1.5 m tall?

Step 1 Write the fraction.

$$\frac{\text{part}}{\text{whole}} = \frac{12}{20}$$

Step 2 To find the GCF of the numerator and denominator, list all of the factors of each number.

Factors of 12: 1, 2, 3, 4, 6, 12 (the numbers that divide evenly into 12)

Factors of 20: 1, 2, 4, 5, 10, 20 (the numbers that divide evenly into 20)

Step 3 List the common factors.

1, 2, 4.

Step 4 Choose the greatest factor in the list of common factors.

The GCF of 12 and 20 is 4.

Step 5 Divide the numerator and denominator by the GCF.

$$\frac{12 \div 4}{20 \div 4} = \frac{3}{5}$$

In the field, $\frac{3}{5}$ of the corn plants are over 1.5 m tall.

Practice Problem There are 90 duck eggs in a population. Of those eggs, 66 hatch over a one-week period. What fraction of the eggs hatch over a one-week period? Write the fraction in simplest form.

Math Skill Handbook

Calculating Ratios

A **ratio** is a comparison of two numbers by division.

Ratios can be written 3 to 5 or 3:5. Ratios also can be written as fractions, such as $\frac{3}{5}$. Ratios, like fractions, can be written in simplest form. Recall that a fraction is in **simplest form** when the greatest common factor (GCF) of the numerator and denominator is 1.

Example From a package of sunflower seeds, 40 seeds germinated and 64 did not. What is the ratio of germinated to not germinated seeds as a fraction in simplest form?

Step 1 Write the ratio as a fraction.

$$\frac{germinated}{not\ germinated} = \frac{40}{64}$$

Step 2 Express the fraction in simplest form. The GCF of 40 and 64 is 8.

$$\frac{40}{64} = \frac{40 \div 8}{64 \div 8} = \frac{5}{8}$$

The ratio of germinated to not germinated seeds is $\frac{5}{8}$.

Practice Problem Two children measure 100 cm and 144 cm in height. What is the ratio of their heights in simplest fraction form?

Using Decimals

A **decimal** is a fraction with a denominator of 10, 100, 1,000, or another power of 10. For example, 0.854 is the same as the fraction $\frac{854}{1,000}$.

In a decimal, the decimal point separates the ones place and the tenths place. For example, 0.27 means twenty-seven hundredths, or $\frac{27}{100}$, where 27 is the **number of units** out of 100 units. Any fraction can be written as a decimal using division.

Example Write $\frac{5}{8}$ as a decimal.

Step 1 Write a division problem with the numerator, 5, as the dividend and the denominator, 8, as the divisor. Write 5 as 5.000.

Step 2 Solve the problem.

$$
\begin{array}{r}
0.625 \\
8{\overline{)5.000}} \\
\underline{48} \\
20 \\
\underline{16} \\
40 \\
\underline{40} \\
0
\end{array}
$$

Therefore, $\frac{5}{8} = 0.625$.

Practice Problem Write $\frac{19}{25}$ as a decimal.

Using Percentages

The word *percent* means "out of one hundred." A **percent** is a ratio that compares a number to 100. Suppose you read that 77 percent of all fish on Earth live in the Pacific Ocean. That is the same as reading that the Earth's fish that live in the Pacific Ocean is $\frac{77}{100}$. To express a fraction as a percent, first find an equivalent decimal for the fraction. Then, multiply the decimal by 100 and add the percent symbol. For example, $\frac{1}{2} = 1 \div 2 = 0.5$. Then $0.5 = 0.50 = 50\%$.

Example Express $\frac{13}{20}$ as a percent.

Step 1 Find the equivalent decimal for the fraction.

$$\begin{array}{r} 0.65 \\ 20\overline{)13.00} \\ \underline{120} \\ 100 \\ \underline{100} \\ 0 \end{array}$$

Step 2 Rewrite the fraction $\frac{13}{20}$ as 0.65.

Step 3 Multiply 0.65 by 100 and add the % sign.

$$0.65 \cdot 100 = 65 = 65\%$$

So, $\frac{13}{20} = 65\%$.

Practice Problem In an experimental population of 365 sheep, 73 were brown. What percent of the sheep were brown?

Using Precision and Significant Digits

When you make a **measurement,** the value you record depends on the precision of the measuring instrument. When adding or subtracting numbers with different precision, the answer is rounded to the smallest number of decimal places of any number in the sum or difference. When multiplying or dividing, the answer is rounded to the smallest number of significant figures of any number being multiplied or divided. When counting the number of **significant figures,** all digits are counted except zeros at the end of a number with no decimal such as 2,500, and zeros at the beginning of a decimal such as 0.03020.

Example The lengths 5.28 and 5.2 are measured in meters. Find the sum of these lengths and report the sum using the least precise measurement.

Step 1 Find the sum.

$$\begin{array}{ll} 5.28 \text{ m} & \text{2 digits after the decimal} \\ \underline{+\ 5.2\ \ \text{m}} & \text{1 digit after the decimal} \\ 10.48 \text{ m} \end{array}$$

Step 2 Round to one digit after the decimal because the least number of digits after the decimal of the numbers being added is 1.

The sum is 10.5 m.

Practice Problem Multiply the numbers in the example using the rule for multiplying and dividing. Report the answer with the correct number of significant figures.

Math Skill Handbook

An **equation** is a statement that two things are equal. For example, $A = B$ is an equation that states that A is equal to B.

Sometimes one side of the equation will contain a **variable** whose value is not known. In the equation $3x = 12$, the variable is x.

The equation is solved when the variable is replaced with a value that makes both sides of the equation equal to each other. For example, the solution of the equation $3x = 12$ is $x = 4$. If the x is replaced with 4, then the equation becomes $3 \cdot 4 = 12$, or $12 = 12$.

To solve an equation such as $8x = 40$, divide both sides of the equation by the number that multiplies the variable.

$$8x = 40$$
$$\frac{8x}{8} = \frac{40}{8}$$
$$x = 5$$

You can check your answer by replacing the variable with your solution and seeing if both sides of the equation are the same.

$$8x = 8 \cdot 5 = 40$$

The left and right sides of the equation are the same, so $x = 5$ is the solution.

Sometimes an equation is written in this way: $a = bc$. This also is called a **formula.** The letters can be replaced by numbers, but the numbers must still make both sides of the equation the same.

Example 1 Solve the equation $10x = 35$.

Step 1 Find the solution by dividing each side of the equation by 10.

$$10x = 35 \qquad \frac{10x}{10} = \frac{35}{10} \qquad x = 3.5$$

Step 2 Check the solution.

$$10x = 35 \qquad 10 \times 3.5 = 35 \qquad 35 = 35$$

Both sides of the equation are equal, so $x = 3.5$ is the solution to the equation.

Example 2 In the formula $a = bc$, find the value of c if $a = 20$ and $b = 2$.

Step 1 Rearrange the formula so the unknown value is by itself on one side of the equation by dividing both sides by b.

$$a = bc$$
$$\frac{a}{b} = \frac{bc}{b}$$
$$\frac{a}{b} = c$$

Step 2 Replace the variables a and b with the values that are given.

$$\frac{a}{b} = c$$
$$\frac{20}{2} = c$$
$$10 = c$$

Step 3 Check the solution.

$$a = bc$$
$$20 = 2 \times 10$$
$$20 = 20$$

Both sides of the equation are equal, so $c = 10$ is the solution when $a = 20$ and $b = 2$.

Practice Problem In the formula $h = gd$, find the value of d if $g = 12.3$ and $h = 17.4$.

Using Proportions

A **proportion** is an equation that shows that two ratios are equivalent. The ratios $\frac{2}{4}$ and $\frac{5}{10}$ are equivalent, so they can be written as $\frac{2}{4} = \frac{5}{10}$. This equation is an example of a proportion.

When two ratios form a proportion, the **cross products** are equal. To find the cross products in the proportion $\frac{2}{4} = \frac{5}{10}$, multiply the 2 and the 10, and the 4 and the 5. Therefore $2 \cdot 10 = 4 \cdot 5$, **or 20 = 20.**

Because you know that both proportions are equal, you can use cross products to find a missing term in a proportion. This is known as **solving the proportion.** Solving a proportion is similar to solving an equation.

Example The heights of a tree and a pole are proportional to the lengths of their shadows. The tree casts a shadow of 24 m at the same time that a 6-m pole casts a shadow of 4 m. What is the height of the tree?

Step 1 Write a proportion.

$$\frac{\text{height of tree}}{\text{height of pole}} = \frac{\text{length of tree's shadow}}{\text{length of pole's shadow}}$$

Step 2 Substitute the known values into the proportion. Let h represent the unknown value, the height of the tree.

$$\frac{h}{6} = \frac{24}{4}$$

Step 3 Find the cross products.

$$h \cdot 4 = 6 \cdot 24$$

Step 4 Simplify the equation.

$$4h = 144$$

Step 5 Divide each side by 4.

$$\frac{4h}{4} = \frac{144}{4}$$

$$h = 36$$

The height of the tree is 36 m.

Practice Problem The proportions of bluefish are stable by the time they reach a length of 30 cm. The distance from the tip of the mouth to the back edge of the gill cover in a 35-cm bluefish is 15 cm. What is the distance from the tip of the mouth to the back edge of the gill cover in a 59-cm bluefish?

Math Skill Handbook

Statistics is the branch of mathematics that deals with collecting, analyzing, and presenting data. In statistics, there are three common ways to summarize the data with a single number—the mean, the median, and the mode.

The **mean** of a set of data is the arithmetic average. It is found by adding the numbers in the data set and dividing by the number of items in the set.

The **median** is the middle number in a set of data when the data are arranged in numerical order. If there were an even number of data points, the median would be the mean of the two middle numbers.

The **mode** of a set of data is the number or item that appears most often.

Another number that often is used to describe a set of data is the range. The **range** is the difference between the largest number and the smallest number in a set of data.

A **frequency table** shows how many times each piece of data occurs, usually in a survey. The frequency table below shows the results of a student survey on favorite color.

Color	Tally	Frequency
red	||||	4
blue	||||	5
black	||	2
green	|||	3
purple	|||| ||	7
yellow	|||| |	6

Based on the frequency table data, which color is the favorite?

Example The high temperatures (in °C) on five consecutive days in a desert habitat under study are 39°, 37°, 44°, 36°, and 44°. Find the mean, median, mode, and range of this set.

To find the mean:
Step 1 Find the sum of the numbers.

$$39 + 37 + 44 + 36 + 44 = 200$$

Step 2 Divide the sum by the number of items, which is 5.

$$200 \div 5 = 40$$

The mean high temperature is 40°C.

To find the median:
Step 1 Arrange the temperatures from least to greatest.

$$36, \ 37, \ \underline{39}, \ 44, \ 44$$

Step 2 Determine the middle temperature.

The median high temperature is 39°C.

To find the mode:
Step 1 Group the numbers that are the same together.

$$44, 44, 36, 37, 39$$

Step 2 Determine the number that occurs most in the set.

$$\underline{44, 44}, 36, 37, 39$$

The mode measure is 44°C.

To find the range:
Step 1 Arrange the temperatures from largest to smallest.

$$44, 44, 39, 37, 36$$

Step 2 Determine the largest and smallest temperature in the set.

$$\underline{44}, 44, 39, 37, \underline{36}$$

Step 3 Find the difference between the largest and smallest temperatures.

$$44 - 36 = 8$$

The range is 8°C.

Practice Problem Find the mean, median, mode, and range for the data set 8, 4, 12, 8, 11, 14, 16.

Safety in the Science Classroom

1. Always obtain your teacher's permission to begin an investigation.

2. Study the procedure. If you have questions, ask your teacher. Be sure you understand any safety symbols shown on the page.

3. Use the safety equipment provided for you. Goggles and a safety apron should be worn during most investigations.

4. Always slant test tubes away from yourself and others when heating them or adding substances to them.

5. Never eat or drink in the lab, and never use lab glassware as food or drink containers. Never inhale chemicals. Do not taste any substances or draw any material into a tube with your mouth.

6. Report any spill, accident, or injury, no matter how small, immediately to your teacher, then follow his or her instructions.

7. Know the location and proper use of the fire extinguisher, safety shower, fire blanket, first aid kit, and fire alarm.

8. Keep all materials away from open flames. Tie back long hair and tie down loose clothing.

9. If your clothing should catch fire, smother it with the fire blanket, or get under a safety shower. NEVER RUN.

10. If a fire should occur, turn off the gas then leave the room according to established procedures.

Follow these procedures as you clean up your work area

1. Turn off the water and gas. Disconnect electrical devices.

2. Clean all pieces of equipment and return all materials to their proper places.

3. Dispose of chemicals and other materials as directed by your teacher. Place broken glass and solid substances in the proper containers. Make sure never to discard materials in the sink.

4. Clean your work area. Wash your hands thoroughly after working in the laboratory.

First Aid	
Injury	**Safe Response ALWAYS NOTIFY YOUR TEACHER IMMEDIATELY**
Burns	Apply cold water.
Cuts and Bruises	Stop any bleeding by applying direct pressure. Cover cuts with a clean dressing. Apply ice packs or cold compresses to bruises.
Fainting	Leave the person lying down. Loosen any tight clothing and keep crowds away.
Foreign Matter in Eye	Flush with plenty of water. Use eyewash bottle or fountain.
Poisoning	Note the suspected poisoning agent.
Any Spills on Skin	Flush with large amounts of water or use safety shower.

Care and Use of a Microscope

Eyepiece Contains magnifying lenses you look through.

Arm Supports the body tube.

Low-power objective Contains the lens with the lowest power magnification.

Stage clips Hold the microscope slide in place.

Fine adjustment Sharpens the image under high magnification.

Coarse adjustment Focuses the image under low power.

Body tube Connects the eyepiece to the revolving nosepiece.

Revolving nosepiece Holds and turns the objectives into viewing position.

High-power objective Contains the lens with the highest magnification.

Stage Supports the microscope slide.

Light source Provides light that passes upward through the diaphragm, the specimen, and the lenses.

Base Provides support for the microscope.

Reference
Handbook

Caring for a Microscope

1. Always carry the microscope holding the arm with one hand and supporting the base with the other hand.

2. Don't touch the lenses with your fingers.

3. The coarse adjustment knob is used only when looking through the lowest-power objective lens. The fine adjustment knob is used when the high-power objective is in place.

4. Cover the microscope when you store it.

Using a Microscope

1. Place the microscope on a flat surface that is clear of objects. The arm should be toward you.

2. Look through the eyepiece. Adjust the diaphragm so light comes through the opening in the stage.

3. Place a slide on the stage so the specimen is in the field of view. Hold it firmly in place by using the stage clips.

4. Always focus with the coarse adjustment and the low-power objective lens first. After the object is in focus on low power, turn the nosepiece until the high-power objective is in place. Use ONLY the fine adjustment to focus with the high-power objective lens.

Making a Wet-Mount Slide

1. Carefully place the item you want to look at in the center of a clean, glass slide. Make sure the sample is thin enough for light to pass through.

2. Use a dropper to place one or two drops of water on the sample.

3. Hold a clean coverslip by the edges and place it at one edge of the water. Slowly lower the coverslip onto the water until it lies flat.

4. If you have too much water or a lot of air bubbles, touch the edge of a paper towel to the edge of the coverslip to draw off extra water and draw out unwanted air.

Diversity of Life: Classification of Living Organisms

A six-kingdom system of classification of organisms is used today. Two kingdoms—Kingdom Archaebacteria and Kingdom Eubacteria—contain organisms that do not have a nucleus and that lack membrane-bound structures in the cytoplasm of their cells. The members of the other four kingdoms have a cell or cells that contain a nucleus and structures in the cytoplasm, some of which are surrounded by membranes. These kingdoms are Kingdom Protista, Kingdom Fungi, Kingdom Plantae, and Kingdom Animalia.

Kingdom Archaebacteria

one-celled; some absorb food from their surroundings; some are photosynthetic; some are chemosynthetic; many found in extremely harsh environments including salt ponds, hot springs, swamps, and deep-sea hydrothermal vents

Kingdom Eubacteria

one-celled; most absorb food from their surroundings; some are photosynthetic; some are chemosynthetic; many are parasites; many are round, spiral, or rod-shaped; some form colonies

Kingdom Protista

Phylum Euglenophyta one-celled; photosynthetic or take in food; most have one flagellum; euglenoids

Phylum Bacillariophyta one-celled; photosynthetic; have unique double shells made of silica; diatoms

Phylum Dinoflagellata one-celled; photosynthetic; contain red pigments; have two flagella; dinoflagellates

Phylum Chlorophyta one-celled, many-celled, or colonies; photosynthetic; contain chlorophyll; live on land, in freshwater, or salt water; green algae

Phylum Rhodophyta most are many-celled; photosynthetic; contain red pigments; most live in deep, saltwater environments; red algae

Phylum Phaeophyta most are many-celled; photosynthetic; contain brown pigments; most live in saltwater environments; brown algae

Phylum Rhizopoda one-celled; take in food; are free-living or parasitic; move by means of pseudopods; amoebas

Kingdom Eubacteria
Bacillus anthracis

Phylum Chlorophyta
Desmids

Amoeba

Phylum Zoomastigina one-celled; take in food; free-living or parasitic; have one or more flagella; zoomastigotes

Phylum Ciliophora one-celled; take in food; have large numbers of cilia; ciliates

Phylum Sporozoa one-celled; take in food; have no means of movement; are parasites in animals; sporozoans

Phylum Myxomycota
Slime mold

Phyla Myxomycota and Acrasiomycota one- or many-celled; absorb food; change form during life cycle; cellular and plasmodial slime molds

Phylum Oomycota many-celled; are either parasites or decomposers; live in freshwater or salt water; water molds, rusts and downy mildews

Kingdom Fungi

Phylum Zygomycota many-celled; absorb food; spores are produced in sporangia; zygote fungi; bread mold

Phylum Ascomycota one- and many-celled; absorb food; spores produced in asci; sac fungi; yeast

Phylum Basidiomycota many-celled; absorb food; spores produced in basidia; club fungi; mushrooms

Phylum Deuteromycota members with unknown reproductive structures; imperfect fungi; *Penicillium*

Mycophycota organisms formed by symbiotic relationship between an ascomycote or a basidiomycote and green alga or cyanobacterium; lichens

Phylum Oomycota
Phytophthora infestans

Lichens

Kingdom Plantae

Divisions Bryophyta (mosses), **Anthocerophyta** (hornworts), **Hepatophytal** (liverworts), **Psilophytal** (whisk ferns) many-celled nonvascular plants; reproduce by spores produced in capsules; green; grow in moist, land environments

Division Lycophyta many-celled vascular plants; spores are produced in conelike structures; live on land; are photosynthetic; club mosses

Division Sphenophyta vascular plants; ribbed and jointed stems; scalelike leaves; spores produced in conelike structures; horsetails

Division Pterophyta vascular plants; leaves called fronds; spores produced in clusters of sporangia called sori; live on land or in water; ferns

Division Ginkgophyta deciduous trees; only one living species; have fan-shaped leaves with branching veins and fleshy cones with seeds; ginkgoes

Division Cycadophyta palmlike plants; have large, featherlike leaves; produces seeds in cones; cycads

Division Coniferophyta deciduous or evergreen; trees or shrubs; have needlelike or scalelike leaves; seeds produced in cones; conifers

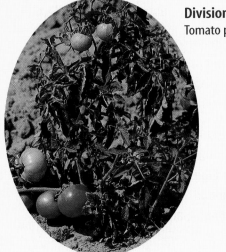

Division Anthophyta
Tomato plant

Phylum Platyhelminthes
Flatworm

Division Gnetophyta shrubs or woody vines; seeds are produced in cones; division contains only three genera; gnetum

Division Anthophyta dominant group of plants; flowering plants; have fruits with seeds

Kingdom Animalia

Phylum Porifera aquatic organisms that lack true tissues and organs; are asymmetrical and sessile; sponges

Phylum Cnidaria radially symmetrical organisms; have a digestive cavity with one opening; most have tentacles armed with stinging cells; live in aquatic environments singly or in colonies; includes jellyfish, corals, hydra, and sea anemones

Phylum Platyhelminthes bilaterally symmetrical worms; have flattened bodies; digestive system has one opening; parasitic and free-living species; flatworms

Division Bryophyta
Liverwort

Phylum Chordata

Phylum Nematoda round, bilaterally symmetrical body; have digestive system with two openings; free-living forms and parasitic forms; roundworms

Phylum Mollusca soft-bodied animals, many with a hard shell and soft foot or footlike appendage; a mantle covers the soft body; aquatic and terrestrial species; includes clams, snails, squid, and octopuses

Phylum Annelida bilaterally symmetrical worms; have round, segmented bodies; terrestrial and aquatic species; includes earthworms, leeches, and marine polychaetes

Phylum Arthropoda largest animal group; have hard exoskeletons, segmented bodies, and pairs of jointed appendages; land and aquatic species; includes insects, crustaceans, and spiders

Phylum Echinodermata marine organisms; have spiny or leathery skin and a water-vascular system with tube feet; are radially symmetrical; includes sea stars, sand dollars, and sea urchins

Phylum Chordata organisms with internal skeletons and specialized body systems; most have paired appendages; all at some time have a notochord, nerve cord, gill slits, and a postanal tail; include fish, amphibians, reptiles, birds, and mammals

This glossary defines each key term that appears in bold type in the text. It also shows the chapter, section, and page number where you can find the words used.

A

active transport: energy-requiring process in which transport proteins bind with particles and move them through a cell membrane. (Chap. 3, Sec. 2, p. 79)

adaptation: any variation that makes an organism better suited to its environment. (Chap. 6, Sec. 1, p. 160)

allele (uh LEEL): an alternate form that a gene may have for a single trait; can be dominant or recessive. (Chap. 5, Sec. 1, p. 129)

asexual reproduction: a type of reproduction—fission, budding, and regeneration—in which a new organism is produced from one parent and has DNA identical to the parent organism. (Chap. 4, Sec. 1, p. 103)

B

binomial nomenclature (bi NOH mee ul · NOH mun klay chur): two-word naming system that gives all organisms their scientific name. (Chap. 1, Sec. 4, p. 22)

biogenesis (bi oh JEN uh suhs): theory that living things come only from other living things. (Chap. 1, Sec. 3, p. 17)

C

cell: smallest unit of an organism that can carry on life functions. (Chap. 1, Sec. 2, p. 12)

cell membrane: protective outer covering of all cells that is made up of a double layer of fatlike molecules and regulates the interaction between the cell and the environment. (Chap. 2, Sec. 1, p. 40)

cell theory: states that all organisms are made up of one or more cells, the cell is the basic unit of life, and all cells come from other cells. (Chap. 2, Sec. 2, p. 53)

cell wall: rigid structure that encloses, supports, and protects the cells of plants, algae, fungi, and most bacteria. (Chap. 2, Sec. 1, p. 41)

chloroplast: green, chlorophyll-containing, plant-cell organelle that converts sunlight, carbon dioxide, and water into sugar. (Chap. 2, Sec. 1, p. 44)

chromosome: structure in a cell's nucleus that contains genetic material. (Chap. 4, Sec. 1, p. 100)

control: standard to which the outcome of a test is compared. (Chap. 1, Sec. 1, p. 7)

cytoplasm: constantly moving gel-like mixture inside the cell membrane that contains heredity material and is the location of most of a cell's life processes. (Chap. 2, Sec. 1, p. 40)

D

diffusion: a type of passive transport in cells in which molecules move from areas where there are more of them to areas where there are fewer of them. (Chap. 3, Sec. 2, p. 77)

diploid (DIHP loyd): cell whose chromosomes occur in pairs. (Chap. 4, Sec. 2, p. 106)

DNA: deoxyribonucleic acid, which is the genetic material of all organisms, made up of two twisted strands of sugar-phosphate molecules and nitrogen bases. (Chap. 4, Sec. 3, p. 112)

dominant (DAHM uh nunt): describes a trait that covers over, or dominates, another form of that trait. (Chap. 5, Sec. 1, p. 131)

English Glossary

E

egg: haploid sex cell formed in the female reproductive organs. (Chap. 4, Sec. 2, p. 106)

embryology (em bree AHL uh jee): study of embryos and their development. (Chap. 6, Sec. 2, p. 169)

endocytosis (en duh si TOH sus): process by which a cell takes in a substance by surrounding it with the cell membrane. (Chap. 3, Sec. 2, p. 80)

endoplasmic reticulum (ER): cytoplasmic organelle that moves materials around in a cell and is made up of a complex series of folded membranes; can be rough (with attached ribosomes) or smooth (without attached ribosomes). (Chap. 2, Sec. 1, p. 45)

enzyme: a type of protein that regulates nearly all chemical reactions in cells. (Chap. 3, Sec. 1, p. 73)

equilibrium: occurs when molecules of one substance are spread evenly throughout another substance. (Chap. 3, Sec. 2, p. 14)

evolution: change in inherited characteristics over time. (Chap. 6, Sec. 1, p. 156)

exocytosis (ek soh si TOH sus): process by which vesicles release their contents outside the cell. (Chap. 3, Sec. 2, p. 80)

F

fermentation: process by which oxygen-lacking cells and some one-celled organisms release small amounts of energy from glucose molecules and produce wastes such as alcohol, carbon dioxide, and lactic acid. (Chap. 3, Sec. 3, p. 86)

fertilization: in sexual reproduction, the joining of a sperm and egg. (Chap. 4, Sec. 2, p. 106)

G

gene: section of DNA on a chromosome that contains instructions for making specific proteins. (Chap. 4, Sec. 3, p. 114)

genetic engineering: biological and chemical methods to change the arrangement of a gene's DNA to improve crop production, produce large volumes of medicine, and change how cells perform their normal functions. (Chap. 5, Sec. 3, p. 144)

genetics (juh NET ihks): the study of how traits are inherited through the actions of alleles. (Chap. 5, Sec. 1, p. 129)

genotype (JEE nuh tipe): an organism's genetic makeup. (Chap. 5, Sec. 1, p. 133)

genus: first word of the two-word scientific name used to identify a group of similar species. (Chap. 1, Sec. 4, p. 22)

Golgi bodies: organelles that package cellular materials and transport them within the cell or out of the cell. (Chap. 2, Sec. 1, p. 45)

gradualism: model describing evolution as a slow process by which one species changes into a new species through a continuing series of mutations and variations over time. (Chap. 6, Sec. 1, p. 162)

H

haploid (HAP loyd): cell that has only one of each type of chromosome. (Chap. 4, Sec. 2, p. 107)

heredity (huh RED ut ee): the passing of traits from parent to offspring. (Chap. 5, Sec. 1, p. 129)

heterozygous (het uh roh ZI gus): describes an organism with two different alleles for a trait. (Chap. 5, Sec. 1, p. 133)

homeostasis: ability of an organism to keep proper internal conditions no matter what external stimuli are occurring. (Chap. 1, Sec. 2, p. 13)

hominid: humanlike primate that appeared about 4 million to 6 million years ago, ate both plants and meat, and walked upright on two legs. (Chap. 6, Sec. 3, p. 173)

homologous (huh MAHL uh gus): body parts that are similar in structure and origin and can be similar in function. (Chap. 6, Sec. 2, p. 170)

Homo sapiens: early humans that likely evolved from Cro-Magnons. (Chap. 6, Sec. 3, p. 175)

homozygous (hoh muh ZI gus): describes an organism with two alleles that are the same for a trait. (Chap. 5, Sec. 1, p. 133)

host cell: living cell in which a virus can actively reproduce or in which a virus can hide until activated by environmental stimuli. (Chap. 2, Sec. 3, p. 54)

hybrid (HI brud): an offspring that was given different genetic information for a trait from each parent. (Chap. 5, Sec. 1, p. 131)

hypothesis: prediction that can be tested. (Chap. 1, Sec. 1, p. 6)

I

incomplete dominance: production of a phenotype that is intermediate between the two homozygous parents. (Chap. 5, Sec. 2, p. 137)

inorganic compound: compound, such as H_2O, that is made from elements other than carbon and whose atoms can usually be arranged in only one structure. (Chap. 3, Sec. 1, p. 73)

K

kingdom: first and largest category used to classify organisms. (Chap. 1, Sec. 4, p. 21)

L

law: statement about how things work in nature that seems to be true consistently. (Chap. 1, Sec. 1, p. 8)

M

meiosis (mi OH sus): reproductive process that produces four haploid sex cells from one diploid cell and ensures offspring will have the same number of chromosomes as the parent organisms. (Chap. 4, Sec. 2, p. 107)

metabolism: the total of all chemical reactions in an organism. (Chap. 3, Sec. 3, p. 83)

mitochondrion: cell organelle that breaks down lipids and carbohydrates and releases energy. (Chap. 2, Sec. 1, p. 44)

mitosis (mi TOH sus): cell process in which the nucleus divides to form two nuclei identical to each other, and identical to the original nucleus, in a series of steps (prophase, metaphase, anaphase, and telophase). (Chap. 4, Sec. 1, p. 100)

mixture: a combination of substances in which the individual substances do not change or combine chemically but instead retain their own individual properties; can be gases, solids, liquids, or any combination of them. (Chap. 3, Sec. 1, p. 71)

mutation: any permanent change in a gene or chromosome of a cell; may be beneficial, harmful, or have little effect on an organism. (Chap. 4, Sec. 3, p. 116)

N

natural selection: organisms with traits best suited to their environment are more likely to survive and reproduce; includes concepts of variation, overproduction, and competition. (Chap. 6, Sec. 1, p. 159)

nucleus: organelle that controls all the activities of a cell and contains hereditary material made of proteins and DNA. (Chap. 2, Sec. 1, p. 42)

O

organ: structure, such as the heart, made up of different types of tissues that all work together. (Chap. 2, Sec. 1, p. 47)

organelle: structure in the cytoplasm of a eukaryotic cell that can act as a storage site, process energy, move materials, or manufacture substances. (Chap. 2, Sec. 1, p. 42)

organic compounds: compounds that always contain hydrogen and carbon; carbohydrates, lipids, proteins, and nucleic acids are organic compounds found in living things. (Chap. 3, Sec. 1, p. 72)

organisms: any living things that are made of cells, use energy, reproduce, respond, and grow and develop. (Chap. 1, Sec. 2, p. 12)

osmosis: a type of passive transport that occurs when water diffuses through a cell membrane. (Chap. 3, Sec. 2, p. 78)

passive transport: movement of substances through a cell membrane without the use of cellular energy; includes diffusion, osmosis, and facilitated diffusion. (Chap. 3, Sec. 2, p. 76)

phenotype (FEE nuh tipe): outward physical appearance and behavior of an organism. (Chap. 5, Sec. 1, p. 133)

photosynthesis: process by which plants and many other producers use light energy from the Sun to make sugars, which can be used as food. (Chap. 3, Sec. 3, p. 84)

phylogeny (fi LAH juh nee): evolutionary history of an organism; used today to group organisms into six kingdoms. (Chap. 1, Sec. 4, p. 21)

polygenic (pahl ih JEHN ihk) **inheritance:** occurs when a group of gene pairs acts together and produces a specific trait, such as human eye color, skin color, or height. (Chap. 5, Sec. 2, p. 139)

primates: group of mammals including humans, monkeys, and apes that share characteristics such as opposable thumbs, binocular vision, and flexible shoulders. (Chap. 6, Sec. 3, p. 172)

punctuated equilibrium: model describing the rapid evolution that occurs when mutation of a few genes results in a species suddenly changing into a new species. (Chap. 6, Sec. 1, p. 162)

Punnett (PUN ut) **square:** a tool to predict the probability of certain traits in offspring that shows the different ways alleles can combine. (Chap. 5, Sec. 1, p. 133)

radioactive element: element that gives off a steady amount of radiation as it slowly changes to a nonradioactive element. (Chap. 6, Sec. 2, p. 167)

recessive (rih SES ihv): describes a trait that is covered over, or dominated, by another form of that trait and seems to disappear. (Chap. 5, Sec. 1, p. 131)

respiration: process by which producers and consumers release stored energy from food molecules. (Chap. 3, Sec. 3, p. 85)

ribosome: small structure on which cells make their own proteins. (Chap. 2, Sec. 1, p. 44)

RNA: ribonucleic acid, which carries codes for making proteins from the nucleus to the ribosomes. (Chap. 4, Sec. 3, p. 114)

S

scientific methods: procedures used to solve problems and answer questions that can include stating the problem, gathering information, forming a hypothesis, testing the hypothesis with an experiment, analyzing data, and drawing conclusions. (Chap. 1, Sec. 1, p. 5)

sedimentary rock: a type of rock, such as limestone, that is most likely to contain fossils and is formed when layers of sand, silt, clay, or mud are cemented and compacted together or when minerals are deposited from a solution. (Chap. 6, Sec. 2, p. 166)

sex-linked gene: an allele inherited on a sex chromosome and that can cause human genetic disorders such as color blindness and hemophilia. (Chap. 5, Sec. 2, p. 142)

sexual reproduction: a type of reproduction in which two sex cells, usually an egg and a sperm, join to form a zygote, which will develop into a new organism with a unique identity. (Chap. 4, Sec. 2, p. 106)

species: group of organisms that share similar characteristics and can reproduce among themselves. (Chap. 6, Sec. 1, p. 156)

sperm: haploid sex cells formed in the male reproductive organs. (Chap. 4, Sec. 2, p. 106)

spontaneous generation: idea that living things come from nonliving things. (Chap. 1, Sec. 3, p. 17)

T

theory: explanation of things or events based on scientific knowledge resulting from many observations and experiments. (Chap. 1, Sec. 1, p. 8)

tissue: group of similar cells that work together to do one job. (Chap. 2, Sec. 1, p. 47)

V

variable: something in an experiment that can change. (Chap. 1, Sec. 1, p. 7)

variation: inherited trait that makes an individual different from other members of the same species and results from a mutation in the organism's genes. (Chap. 6, Sec. 1, p. 160)

vestigial (veh STIHJ ee ul) **structure:** structure, such as the human appendix, that doesn't seem to have a function and may once have functioned in the body of an ancestor. (Chap. 6, Sec. 2, p. 170)

virus: a strand of hereditary material surrounded by a protein coating. (Chap. 2, Sec. 3, p. 54)

Z

zygote: new diploid cell formed when a sperm fertilizes an egg; will divide by mitosis and develop into a new organism. (Chap. 4, Sec. 2, p. 106)

Spanish Glossary

Este glossario define cada término clave que aparece en negrillas en el texto. También muestra el capítulo, la sección y el número de página en donde se usa dicho término.

A

active transport / transporte activo: proceso que requiere energía en el cual las proteínas de transporte se enlazan con partículas y se mueven a través de la membrana celular. (Cap. 3, Sec. 2, pág. 79)

adaptation / adaptación: toda variación que le permite a un organismo adaptarse mejor a su ambiente. (Cap. 6, Sec. 1, pág. 160)

allele / alelo: formas alternas que un gene puede tener para un sólo rasgo; puede ser dominante o recesivo. (Cap. 5, Sec. 1, pág. 129)

asexual reproduction / reproducción asexual: tipo de reproducción que comprende la fisión, la gemación y la regeneración, en el cual un progenitor produce un nuevo organismo que tiene el DNA idéntico al del organismo progenitor. (Cap. 4, Sec. 1, pág. 103)

B

binomial nomenclature / nomenclatura binaria: sistema que se usa para nombrar organismos y que está basado en dos palabras, la primera palabra indica el género y la segunda palabra indica la especie. (Cap. 1, Sec. 4, pág. 22)

biogenesis / biogénesis: teoría que establece que todo ser vivo proviene de otros seres vivos. (Cap. 1, Sec. 3, pág. 17)

C

cell / célula: unidad básica de los seres vivos que puede realizar las funciones vitales; tiene una estructura ordenada y contiene material hereditario (Cap. 1, Sec. 2, pág. 12)

cell membrane / membrana celular: cubierta externa protectora de todas las células; formada por una capa doble de moléculas adiposas y controla la interacción entre la célula y el medio ambiente. (Cap. 2, Sec. 1, pág. 40)

cell theory / teoría celular: establece que todos los organismos están formados por una o más células, la célula es la unidad básica de la vida y todas las células provienen de otras células. (Cap. 2, Sec. 2, pág. 53)

cell wall / pared celular: estructura rígida que encierra, sostiene y protege las células vegetales, las células de las algas, de los hongos y de la mayoría de las bacterias. (Cap. 2, Sec. 1, pág. 41)

chloroplast / cloroplasto: organelo de las células vegetales, de color verde y que contiene clorofila, que convierte la luz solar, el dióxido de carbono y el agua en azúcar. (Cap. 2, Sec. 1. pág. 44)

chromosome / cromosoma: estructura en el núcleo de una célula que contiene el material genético. (Cap. 4, Sec. 1, pág. 100)

control / control: el estándar que sirve para comparar los resultados obtenidos en un experimento. (Cap. 1, Sec. 1, pág. 7)

cytoplasm / citoplasma: mezcla gelatinosa en continuo movimiento dentro de la membrana celular que contiene material hereditario y en la cual se lleva a cabo la mayoría de los procesos de una célula. (Cap. 2, Sec. 1, pág. 40)

D

diffusion / difusión: tipo de transporte pasivo celular en el que las moléculas se mueven desde áreas de mayor concentración a áreas de menor concentración. (Cap. 3, Sec. 2, pág. 77)

diploid / diploide: célula cuyos cromosomas se dan en pares. (Cap. 4, Sec. 2, pág. 106)

DNA / DNA: ácido desoxirribonucleico; material genético de todos los organismos y compuesto de dos hebras retorcidas de moléculas de fosfato de azúcar y bases nitrogenadas. (Cap. 4, Sec. 3, pág. 112)

dominant / dominante: describe un rasgo que cubre o domina otra forma de dicho rasgo. (Cap. 5, Sec. 1, pág. 131)

E

egg / óvulo: célula haploide formada en los órganos reproductores femeninos. (Cap. 4, Sec. 2, pág. 106)

embryology / embriología: estudio de los embriones y su desarrollo. (Cap. 6, Sec. 2, pág. 169)

endocytosis / endocitosis: proceso que permite que una célula deje pasar una sustancia al rodearla con la membrana celular. (Cap. 3, Sec. 2, pág. 80)

endoplasmic reticulum (ER) / retículo endoplásmico: organelo citoplásmico que mueve materiales dentro de una célula y que está formado por una serie compleja de membranas plegadas; puede ser áspero (con ribosomas adheridos) o liso (sin ribosomas adheridos). (Cap. 2, Sec. 1, pág. 45)

enzyme / enzima: tipo de proteína que regula casi todas las reacciones químicas de las células. (Cap. 3, Sec. 1, pág. 73)

equilibrium / equilibrio: ocurre cuando las moléculas de una sustancia se esparcen uniformemente en otra sustancia. (Cap. 3, Sec. 2, pág. 14)

evolution / evolución: cambio, con el tiempo, en las características heredadas. (Cap. 6, Sec. 1, pág. 156)

exocytosis / exocitosis: proceso a través del cual las vesículas liberan sus contenidos fuera de la célula. (Cap. 3, Sec. 2, pág. 80)

F

fermentation / fermentación: proceso en que las células carentes de oxígeno y algunos organismos unicelulares liberan pequeñas cantidades de energía de las moléculas de glucosa y producen desechos como el alcohol, el dióxido de carbono y el ácido láctico. (Cap. 3, Sec. 3, pág. 86)

fertilization / fecundación: en la reproducción sexual, la unión del espermatozoide y del óvulo. (Cap. 4, Sec. 2, pág. 106)

G

gene / gene: sección de DNA en un cromosoma que contiene las instrucciones para la elaboración de proteínas específicas. (Cap. 4, Sec. 3, pág. 114)

genetic engineering / ingeniería genética: métodos biológicos y químicos que se usan para cambiar el arreglo del DNA de un gene con el propósito de mejorar la producción de cosechas, producir grandes volúmenes de medicamentos y cambiar el funcionamiento normal de células. (Cap. 5, Sec. 3, pág. 144)

genetics / genética: estudia la manera en que se heredan los rasgos a través de las acciones de los alelos. (Cap. 5, Sec. 1, pág. 129)

genotype / genotipo: la composición genética de un organismo. (Cap. 5, Sec. 1, pág. 133)

genus / género: grupo de especies similares. (Cap. 1, Sec. 4, pág. 22)

Golgi bodies / cuerpos de Golgi: organelos que almacenan materiales celulares y los transportan dentro o fuera de la célula. (Cap. 2, Sec. 1, pág. 45)

gradualism / gradualismo: modelo que describe la evolución como un proceso lento mediante el cual una especie se transforma en otra especie, a través de una serie continua de mutaciones y variaciones que ocurren con el paso del tiempo. (Cap. 6, Sec. 1, pág. 162)

haploid / haploide: célula que sólo tiene uno de cada tipo de cromosoma. (Cap. 4, Sec. 2, pág. 107)

heredity / herencia: el traspaso de rasgos de los progenitores a la progenie. (Cap. 5, Sec. 1, pág. 129)

heterozygous / heterocigoto: describe al organismo que presenta dos alelos distintos para un rasgo. (Cap. 5, Sec. 1, pág. 133)

homeostasis / homeostasis: característica de los seres vivos que les permite mantener las condiciones internas adecuadas, a pesar de los cambios en su ambiente. (Cap. 1, Sec. 2, pág. 13)

hominid / homínido: primate de aspecto humano que apareció entre hace 4 millones y 6 millones de años, se alimentaba de plantas y animales y

caminaba derecho en dos piernas. (Cap. 6, Sec. 3, pág. 173)

homologous / homólogo: partes corporales semejantes en estructura y origen y que pueden ser semejantes en cuanto a su función. (Cap. 6, Sec. 2, pág. 170)

Homo sapiens / Homo sapiens: los primeros humanos que probablemente evolucionaron de los hombres de Cro-Magnon. (Cap. 6, Sec. 3, pág. 175)

homozygous / homocigoto: describe un organismo con dos alelos idénticos para el mismo rasgo. (Cap. 5, Sec. 1, pág. 133)

host cell / célula huésped: célula viva en la cual un virus se puede reproducir activamente o en la cual un virus puede ocultarse hasta que los estímulos ambientales lo activen. (Cap. 2, Sec. 3, pág. 54)

hybrid / híbrido: progenie que ha obtenido información genética distinta para un rasgo de cada progenitor. (Cap. 5, Sec. 1, pág. 131)

hypothesis / hipótesis: predicción que se puede poner a prueba. (Cap. 1, Sec. 1, pág. 6)

incomplete dominance / dominancia incompleta: la producción de un fenotipo intermedio al de los dos progenitores homocigotos. (Cap. 5, Sec. 2, pág. 137)

inorganic compound / compuesto orgánico: compuesto cuyos constituyentes son otros elementos, en vez del carbono y cuyos átomos por lo general pueden arreglarse en sólo una estructura, como por ejemplo, el H_2O, (Cap. 3, Sec. 1, pág. 73)

kingdom / reino: la primera y más grande categoría del sistema de clasificación de los organismos; se divide en grupos más pequeños: filo, clase, orden, familia, género y especie. (Cap. 1, Sec. 4, pág. 21)

L

law / ley: enunciado científico que describe cómo ocurren ciertos fenómenos en la naturaleza y que parece ser cierto en todo momento. (Cap. 1, Sec. 1, pág. 8)

M

meiosis / meiosis: proceso reproductor que produce cuatro células sexuales haploides a partir de una célula diploide y asegura que la progenie tenga el mismo número de cromosomas que el organismo progenitor. (Cap. 4, Sec. 2, pág. 107)

metabolism / metabolismo: el total de todas las reacciones químicas en un organismo. (Cap. 3, Sec. 3, pág. 83)

mitochondrion / mitocondria: organelo celular que descompone lípidos y carbohidratos y libera energía. (Cap. 2, Sec. 1, pág. 44)

mitosis / mitosis: proceso celular en que el núcleo se divide para formar dos núcleos idénticos uno al otro e idénticos al núcleo original, en una serie de pasos (profase, metafase, anafase y telofase). (Cap. 4, Sec. 1, pág. 100)

mixture / mezcla: combinación de sustancias en que las sustancias individuales no cambian ni se combinan químicamente, sino que retienen sus propiedades individuales; pueden ser gases, líquidos o cualquier combinación de estos dos. (Cap. 3, Sec. 1, pág. 71)

mutation / mutuación: cualquier cambio permanente en un gene o en un cromosoma de una célula; puede ser beneficioso, perjudicial o puede tener un efecto mínimo en un organismo. (Cap. 4, Sec. 3, pág. 116)

N

natural selection / selección natural: significa que los organismos con rasgos mejor adaptados a su ambiente están más propensos a sobrevivir y reproducirse; incluye conceptos de variación, sobreproducción y competencia. (Cap. 6, Sec. 1, pág. 159)

nucleus / núcleo: organelo que controla todas las actividades de una célula y contiene material hereditario compuesto por proteínas y DNA. (Cap. 2, Sec. 1, pág. 42)

organ / órgano: estructura, como el corazón, compuesta por tipos diferentes de tejidos que funcionan en conjunto. (Cap. 2, Sec. 1, pág. 47)

organelle / organelo: estructura en el citoplasma de una célula eucariota que puede actuar como un lugar de almacenamiento, puede procesar energía, mover materiales o elaborar sustancias. (Cap. 2, Sec. 1, pág. 42)

organic compounds / compuestos orgánicos: compuestos que siempre contienen hidrógeno y carbono; los lípidos, las proteínas y los ácidos nucleicos son compuestos orgánicos que se encuentran en los seres vivos. (Cap. 3, Sec. 1, pág. 72)

organisms / organismo: cualquier ser vivo; usa energía, está formado por células, se reproduce, responde a estímulos, crece y se desarrollan. (Cap. 1, Sec. 2, pág. 12)

osmosis / ósmosis: tipo de transporte pasivo que se lleva a cabo cuando el agua se difunde a través de la membrana celular. (Cap. 3, Sec. 2, pág. 78)

passive transport / transporte pasivo: movimiento de sustancias a través de la membrana celular que no involucra el uso de energía celular; incluye la difusión, la ósmosis y la difusión facilitada. (Cap. 3, Sec. 2, pág. 76)

phenotype / fenotipo: apariencia física externa y comportamiento de un organismo. (Cap. 5, Sec. 1, pág. 133)

photosynthesis / fotosíntesis: proceso mediante el cual las plantas y muchos otros productores utilizan la energía luminosa del Sol para elaborar azúcares que pueden usar como alimento. (Cap. 3, Sec. 3, pág. 84)

phylogeny / filogenia: historia evolutiva de un organismo, sirve para que los científicos puedan clasificar los organismos en reinos. (Cap. 1, Sec. 4, pág. 21)

polygenic inheritance / herencia poligénica: tipo de herencia que ocurre cuando un grupo de pares de genes actúan en conjunto y producen un rasgo específico; por ejemplo el color de los ojos, cabello, piel o estatura de los humanos. (Cap. 5, Sec. 2, pág. 139)

primates / primates: grupo de mamíferos que incluye, entre otros, a los seres humanos, los monos y los simios, los cuales comparten características como pulgares oponibles, visión binocular y hombros flexibles. (Cap. 6, Sec. 3, pág. 172)

punctuated equilibrium / equilibrio puntuado: modelo que describe la evolución rápida que ocurre cuando la mutación de unos cuantos genes da como resultado una especie que repentinamente se transforma en otra especie. (Cap. 6, Sec. 1, pág. 162)

Punnett square / cuadrado de Punnett: instrumento que se usa para predecir ciertos rasgos en la progenie, que muestra las distintas maneras en que los alelos se pueden combinar. (Cap. 5, Sec. 1, pág. 133)

radioactive element / elemento radiactivo: elemento que emite una cantidad constante de radiación a medida que se transforma lentamente en un elemento no radiactivo. (Cap. 6, Sec. 2, pág. 167)

recessive / recesivo: describe un rasgo que es cubierto o dominado por otra forma de ese rasgo y, por lo tanto, parece desaparecer. (Cap. 5, Sec. 1, pág. 131)

respiration / respiración: proceso en que los productores y los consumidores liberan la energía almacenada en las partículas de alimento. (Cap. 3, Sec. 3, pág. 85)

ribosome / ribosoma: estructura pequeña en la cual las células producen sus propias proteínas. (Cap. 2, Sec. 1, pág. 44)

RNA / RNA: ácido ribonucleico que lleva consigo los códigos para la elaboración de proteínas del núcleo a los ribosomas. (Cap. 4, Sec. 3, pág. 114)

scientific method / método científico: técnicas para solucionar problemas que sirven para investigar observaciones realizadas acerca de seres vivos o materia inerte; incluye los siguientes pasos: reconocer un problema, recoger información, formular y poner a prueba una hipótesis, analizar datos y sacar conclusiones. (Cap. 1, Sec. 1, pág. 5)

sedimentary rock / roca sedimentaria: tipo de roca, como la piedra caliza, que está más propensa a contener fósiles y que se forma cuando se cementan o compactan las capas de arena, lodo, arcilla o fango o cuando los minerales se depositan de una solución. (Cap. 6, Sec. 2, pág. 166)

sex-linked gene / gene ligado al sexo: un alelo heredado en un cromosoma del sexo y que puede causar trastornos genéticos, como por ejemplo, el daltonismo o la hemofilia. (Cap. 5, Sec. 2, pág. 142)

sexual reproduction / reproducción sexual: tipo de reproducción en que dos células sexuales, por lo general un óvulo y un espermatozoide, se unen formando un cigoto, el cual se desarrolla en un nuevo organismo con su propia identidad. (Cap. 4, Sec. 2, pág. 106)

species / especies: grupo de organismos que comparten características semejantes y que pueden procrear entre sí. (Cap. 6, Sec. 1, pág. 156)

sperm / espermatozoide: célula sexual haploide formada en los órganos reproductores masculinos. (Cap. 4, Sec. 2, pág. 106)

spontaneous generation / generación espontánea: teoría que dice que los seres vivos pueden originarse a partir de la materia inerte. (Cap. 1, Sec. 3, pág. 17)

theory / teoría: explicación de fenómenos o cosas basada en el conocimiento científico generado a partir de múltiples observaciones y pruebas. (Cap. 1, Sec. 1, pág. 8)

tissue / tejido: grupo de células semejantes que funcionan juntas para efectuar una tarea. (Cap. 2, Sec. 1, pág. 47)

variable / variable: cada una de las condiciones que pueden cambiar durante un experimento. (Cap. 1, Sec. 1, pág. 7)

variation / variación: rasgo heredado que diferencia a un individuo de otros miembros de la misma especie y que resulta de una mutación de los genes del organismo. (Cap. 6, Sec. 1, pág. 160)

vestigial structure / estructura vestigial: estructura, como el apéndice humano, que no parece cumplir función alguna y que tal vez pudo haber funcionado en el cuerpo de un antepasado. (Cap. 6, Sec. 2, pág. 170)

virus / virus: estructura que contiene material hereditario rodeado por un revestimiento proteico y que sólo se desarrolla en el interior de organismos vivos. (Cap. 2, Sec. 3, pág. 54)

zygote / cigoto: nueva célula diploide que se forma cuando un espermatozoide fecunda un óvulo; se divide mediante mitosis y se desarrolla en un nuevo organismo. (Cap. 4, Sec. 2, pág. 106)

Index

The index for *Life's Structure and Function* will help you locate major topics in the book quickly and easily. Each entry in the index is followed by the number of the pages on which the entry is discussed. A page number given in boldfaced type indicates the page on which that entry is defined. A page number given in italic type indicates a page on which the entry is used in an illustration or photograph. The abbreviation *act.* indicates a page on which the entry is used in an activity.

Index

Index

Index

Index

Art Credits

Glencoe would like to acknowledge the artists and agencies who participated in illustrating this program: Absolute Science Illustration; Andrew Evansen; Argosy; Articulate Graphics; Craig Attebery represented by Frank & Jeff Lavaty; CHK America; Gagliano Graphics; Pedro Julio Gonzalez represented by Melissa Turk & The Artist Network; Robert Hynes represented by Mendola Ltd.; Morgan Cain & Associates; JTH Illustration; Laurie O'Keefe; Matthew Pippin represented by Beranbaum Artist's Representative; Precision Graphics; Publisher's Art; Rolin Graphics, Inc.; Wendy Smith represented by Melissa Turk & The Artist Network; Kevin Torline represented by Berendsen and Associates, Inc.; WILDlife ART; Phil Wilson represented by Cliff Knecht Artist Representative; Zoo Botanica.

Photo Credits

Abbreviation Key: AA=Animals Animals; AH=Aaron Haupt; AMP=Amanita Pictures; BC=Bruce Coleman, Inc.; CB=CORBIS; DM=Doug Martin; DRK=DRK Photo; ES=Earth Scenes; FP=Fundamental Photographs; GH=Grant Heilman Photography; IC=Icon Images; KS=KS Studios; LA=Liaison Agency; MB=Mark Burnett; MM=Matt Meadows; PE=PhotoEdit; PD=PhotoDisc; PQ=PictureQuest; PR=Photo Researchers; SB=Stock Boston; TSA=Tom Stack & Associates; TSM=The Stock Market; VU=Visuals Unlimited.

Cover Andrew Syred/Science Photo Library/PR; **v**(l r)Runk/Schoenberger from GH; **vii** TSA; **ix** (t)TSA, (b)Joy Spurr/PR; **2-3** Bob Jacobson/International Stock; **3** Richard Hutchings/PE; **4** Courtesy of ABI PRISM; **5** (t)Dominic Obershaw, (c)AH, (b)Dr. John Carpten; **6** Mickey Gibson/AA; **6-7** A. Witte/C. Mahaney/Stone; **7** Joanne Huemoeller/AA; **8** Kjell B. Sandved/VU; **10 11** MB; **13** Tek Image/Science Photo Library/PR; **14 15** MB; **16** (t)Michael Abbey/Science Source/PR, (c)VU/Michael Delannoy, (b)AH; **17** MB; **18** (t, l to r)Dwight Kuhn, Dwight Kuhn, A. Glauberman/PR, MB, (b, l to r)Runk/ Schoenberger from GH, Dwight Kuhn, Runk/ Schoenberger from GH, Runk/Schoenberger from GH; **19** (t)Bill Beaty/AA,

(bl)Tom & Therisa Stack/TSA, (br)Michael Fogden/ES; **20** AH; **21** Geoff Butler; **22** (tl)Dover Pictorial Archive, (b)Johnny Autrey, (others)Janet Dell Russell Johnson; **24** (t)Arthur C. Smith III from GH, (bl)Hal Beral/VU, (br)Larry L. Miller/PR; **25** Doug Perrine/Innerspace Visions; **26** (l)Brandon D. Cole, (r)Gregory Ochocki/PR; **27** (l)R. Andrew Odum/Peter Arnold, (r)Zig Leszczynski/AA; **28** Alvin E. Staffan; **29** Geoff Butler; **30** (t)Jan Hinsch/Science Photo Library/PR, (b)MB; **31** MB; **32** (l)Eraldo Peres/AP, (r)Marc Von Roosmalen/AP; **33** Marc Von Roosmalen/AP; **34** (tl)Jeff Greenberg/Rainbow, (tr)Hans Pfletschinger/Peter Arnold, (bl)Peter B. Kaplan/PR, (bc)John T. Fowler, (br)Milton Rand/TSA; **35** (l)MB, (r)Will & Deni McIntyre/PR; **38** Oliver Meckes/E.O.S./MPI-Tubingen/PR; **38-39** Tim Flach/Stone; **39** MM; **41** David M. Phillips/VU; **42** (t)Don Fawcett/PR, (b)M. Schliwa/PR; **44** (t)George B. Chapman/VU, (b)P. Motta & T. Naguro/Science Photo Library/PR; **45** (t)Don Fawcett/PR, (b)Biophoto Associates/PR; **49** (l)Biophoto Associates/PR, (r)MM; **50** (bkgd)David M. Phillips/VU, (t)Kathy Talaro/VU, (cl)courtesy Nikon Instruments Inc., (c)Michael Gabridge/VU, (cr)Mike Abbey/VU, (bl br)David M. Phillips/VU; **51** (tl)James W. Evarts, (tr)Bob Krist/CB, (cl)courtesy Olympus Corporation, (cr)Mike Abbey/VU, (bl)Karl Aufderheide/VU, (br)Lawrence Migdale/SB/PQ; **54** (l)Richard J. Green/PR, (c)Dr. J.F.J.M. van der Heuvel, (r)Gelderblom/Eye of Science/PR; **57** Pam Wilson/TX Dept. of Health; **58** (t)AMP, (b)MM; **59** MM; **60** (t)Quest/Science Photo Library/PR, (b)courtesy California Univ.; **61** Nancy Kedersha/Immunogen/Science Photo Library/PR; **62** (t)Oliver Meckes/PR, (b)CDC/ Science Photo Library/PR; **63** (l)Keith Porter/PR, (r)NIBSC/Science Photo Library/PR; **64** Biophoto Associates/Science Source/PR; **66** Bill Longcore/PR; **66-67** KS; **67** AH; **69** Bob Daemmrich; **71** (t)Runk/ Schoenberger from GH, (b)Klaus Guldbrandsen/Science Photo Library/PR; **76** (l)John Fowler, (r)Richard Hamilton Smith/CB; **77** KS; **78** AH; **79** VU; **80** Biophoto Associates/ Science Source/PR; **81** Stephen R. Wagner; **82** MM; **83** AH; **84** Craig Lovell/CB; **85** John Fowler; **86** David M. Phillips/VU; **87** (l)GH, (r)Bios (Klein/Hubert)/Peter

Arnold, Inc.; **88** (t)Runk/Schoenberger from GH, (b)AH; **89** MM; **90** Lappa/Marquart; **91** The Just/Garcia/Hill Science Web Site; **92** (tl)Michael Pogany/Columbus Zoo, (tr)Bachman/PR, (b)Jim Strawser from GH; **93** CNRI/ Science Photo Library/PR; **96** Biophoto Associates/PR; **96-97** Zig Leszcynski/AA; **97** MM; **98** (l)Dave B. Fleetham/ TSA, (r)Cabisco/VU; **100** Cabisco/VU; **101** (t)Michael Abbey/VU, (others)John D. Cunningham/VU; **102** (l)MM, (r)Nigel Cattlin/PR; **103** (l)Barry L. Runk from GH, (r)Runk/Schoenberger from GH; **104** (l)Walker England/ PR, (r)TSA; **105** Runk/Schoenberger from GH; **106** David M. Phillips/The Population Council/PR; **107** (t)Gerald & Buff Corsi/VU, (c)Fred Bruenner/Peter Arnold, Inc., (b)Susan McCartney/PR; **109** (l)John D. Cunningham/ VU, (c)Jen & Des Bartlett/BC, (r)Breck P. Kent; **110** (tl)Artville, (tr)Tim Fehr, (c)Bob Daemmrich/SB/PQ, (bl)Troy Mary Parlee/Index Stock/PQ, (br)Jeffery Myers/Southern Stock/PQ; **116** Stewart Cohen/Stone; **118** (t)Tom McHugh/PR, (b)file photo; **119** Monica Dalmasso/Stone; **120** Philip Lee Harvey/Stone; **121** Lester V. Bergman/CB; **122** (t)John Mitchell/PR, (c)Camille Tokerud/PR, (b)David Scharf/Peter Arnold, Inc.; **123** (l)D. Yeske/VU, (r)GH; **126** David Phillips/Science Source/PR; **126-127** MB; **127** Geoff Butler; **128** Stewart Cohen/Stone; **131** (bkgd)Jane Grushow from GH, (lr)Special Collections, National Agriculture Library; **132** Barry L. Runk From GH; **134** Richard Hutchings/PR; **136** (t)Robert Maier/AA, (b)Gemma Giannini from GH; **137** Gemma Giannini from GH; **138** Dan McCoy from Rainbow; **139** (l)Phil Roach/Ipol, (r)CNRI/Science Photo Library/PR; **140** Gopal Murti/PhotoTake NYC; **141** Tim Davis/PR; **142** (l)Alan & Sandy Carey/PR, (r)Renee Stockdale/AA; **145** Tom Meyers/PR; **146** (t)Runk/ Schoenberger from GH, (b)MB; **147** Laura Sefferlin; **149** KS; **150** David R. Frazier Photolibrary; **154** Bios (Klein & Hubert)/Peter Arnold, Inc.; **154-155** Nigel Cattlin/Holt Studio International/PR; **155** AH; **157** Barbara Cushman/DRK; **158** (l)Tim Davis/PR, (c r)Tui De Roy/Minden Pictures; **160** (l)Gregory G. Dimijian, M.D./PR, (r)Patti Murray/AA; **161** (t)Darek Karp/AA, (b)Vonorla Photography; **162** (l)Joe McDonald/AA, (c)Tom McHugh/PR, (r)Tim Davis/PR; **163** James Richardson/VU; **163** Frans Lanting/Minden Pictures; **165** (l)Dominique Braud/ES, (c)Carr Clifton/Minden Pictures, (r)John Cancalosi/DRK; **166** (bl)John Cancalosi/DRK, (t)Larry Ulrich/DRK, (cl)Ken Lucas/VU, (cr)John Cancalosi/Peter Arnold, Inc., (b)Sinclair Stammers/Science Photo Library/PR; **167** John Kieffer/Peter Arnold, Inc.; **170** (l)Kees Van Den Berg/PR, (r)DM; **171** Peter Veit/DRK; **172** (l)Mark E. Gibson, (r)Gerard Lacz/AA; **173** (tl)Michael Dick/AA, (tr)Carolyn A. McKeone, (b)John Reader/Science Photo Library/PR; **174** (l)John Reader/Science Photo Library/PR, (r)Archivo Iconografico, S.A./CB; **175** Francois Ducasse/Rapho/PR; **176** Kenneth W. Fink/PR; **176-177** AH; **178** (t)Lara Jo Regan/Saba Press Photos, (b)VCG/FPG; **180** (tl)Fritz Polking/VU, (tr)Dan Guravich/PR, (bl)Pascal Goetgheluck/Science Photo Library/PR, (br)Joe McDonald/VU; **181** (l)Koster-Survival/AA, (r)Stephen J. Krasemann/DRK; **182** Tom Tietz/Stone; **186-187** PD; **188** (t)Carolyn A. McKeone/PR, (b)J. & P. Wegner/AA; **189** (tl)Yann Arthus-Bertrand/CB, (tr)Barbara Reed/AA, (bl)Chanan Photography, (br)J-L Klein & M-L Hubert/ Okapia/Photo Researchers; **190** (tl)Renee Stockdale/AA, (tr)Joan Baron/PR, (bl)Carolyn A. McKeone/PR, (br)Yann Arthus-Bertrand/CB; **191** (tl)Stephen Green/TSM, (tr)J & P Wagner/AA, (bl)Jane Howard/PR, (br)Ulrike Schanz/AA; **192** Timothy Fuller; **196** First Image; **199** Dominic Oldershaw; **200** StudiOhio; **201** First Image; **203** Richard Day/AA; **206** Paul Barton/TSM; **209** Charles Gupton/TSM; **218** MM; **219** (t)NIBSC/Science Photo Library/PR, (bl)Dr. Richard Kessel, (br)David John/VU; **220** (t)Runk/Schoenberger from GH, (bl)Andrew Syred/Science Photo Library/PR, (br)Rich Brommer; **221** (t)G.R. Roberts, (bl)Ralph Reinhold/ES, (br)Scott Johnson/AA; **222** Martin Harvey/DRK.

PERIODIC TABLE OF THE ELEMENTS

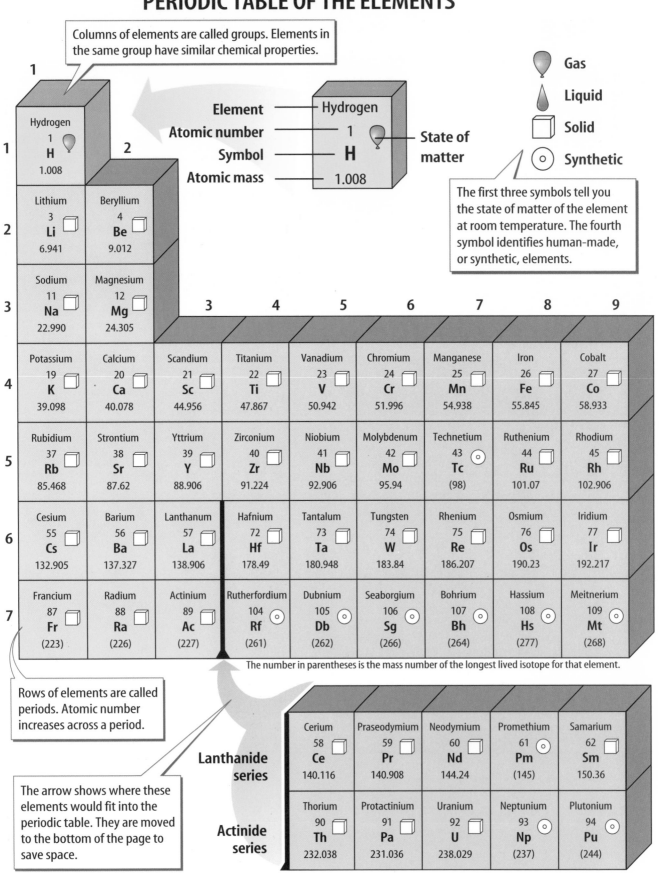

Columns of elements are called groups. Elements in the same group have similar chemical properties.

Element — Hydrogen
Atomic number — 1
Symbol — **H**
Atomic mass — 1.008
State of matter

Gas
Liquid
Solid
Synthetic

The first three symbols tell you the state of matter of the element at room temperature. The fourth symbol identifies human-made, or synthetic, elements.

1	2	3	4	5	6	7	8	9
Hydrogen 1 **H** 1.008								
Lithium 3 **Li** 6.941	Beryllium 4 **Be** 9.012							
Sodium 11 **Na** 22.990	Magnesium 12 **Mg** 24.305							
Potassium 19 **K** 39.098	Calcium 20 **Ca** 40.078	Scandium 21 **Sc** 44.956	Titanium 22 **Ti** 47.867	Vanadium 23 **V** 50.942	Chromium 24 **Cr** 51.996	Manganese 25 **Mn** 54.938	Iron 26 **Fe** 55.845	Cobalt 27 **Co** 58.933
Rubidium 37 **Rb** 85.468	Strontium 38 **Sr** 87.62	Yttrium 39 **Y** 88.906	Zirconium 40 **Zr** 91.224	Niobium 41 **Nb** 92.906	Molybdenum 42 **Mo** 95.94	Technetium 43 **Tc** (98)	Ruthenium 44 **Ru** 101.07	Rhodium 45 **Rh** 102.906
Cesium 55 **Cs** 132.905	Barium 56 **Ba** 137.327	Lanthanum 57 **La** 138.906	Hafnium 72 **Hf** 178.49	Tantalum 73 **Ta** 180.948	Tungsten 74 **W** 183.84	Rhenium 75 **Re** 186.207	Osmium 76 **Os** 190.23	Iridium 77 **Ir** 192.217
Francium 87 **Fr** (223)	Radium 88 **Ra** (226)	Actinium 89 **Ac** (227)	Rutherfordium 104 **Rf** (261)	Dubnium 105 **Db** (262)	Seaborgium 106 **Sg** (266)	Bohrium 107 **Bh** (264)	Hassium 108 **Hs** (277)	Meitnerium 109 **Mt** (268)

The number in parentheses is the mass number of the longest lived isotope for that element.

Rows of elements are called periods. Atomic number increases across a period.

The arrow shows where these elements would fit into the periodic table. They are moved to the bottom of the page to save space.

Lanthanide series	Cerium 58 **Ce** 140.116	Praseodymium 59 **Pr** 140.908	Neodymium 60 **Nd** 144.24	Promethium 61 **Pm** (145)	Samarium 62 **Sm** 150.36
Actinide series	Thorium 90 **Th** 232.038	Protactinium 91 **Pa** 231.036	Uranium 92 **U** 238.029	Neptunium 93 **Np** (237)	Plutonium 94 **Pu** (244)